TALES OF RANNOCH

Errata

Page 12 line 2 'along' becomes 'alone'.

Page 14 Note 2 delete 'as you face it'.

Page 14 Note 5 'Alexander Cameron' becomes 'Alexander Stewart'.

Page 16 7 lines from the bottom 'so shean' becomes 'cheann'.

Page 18 line 19 'Ladashach' becomes 'Ladasach'.

Page 19 14 lines from the bottom 'son' becomes 'sons'.

Page 23 line 8 'lead' becomes 'led'.

Page 31 line 12 'nearly' becomes 'neatly'.

Page 88 line 6 'Loch' becomes 'Lochan'.

Page 98 10 lines from the bottom 'lessoned' becomes 'lessened'.

Page 124 line 1 'or' becomes 'of'.

Page 141 line 7 delete '(or the Horse Loch)'.

Page 144 3 lines from the bottom 'be' becomes 'by'.

TALES OF RANNOCH

BY

A.D. CUNNINGHAM

A.D. CUNNINGHAM
and
Perth & Kinross District Libraries 1989

by the same author

A HISTORY OF RANNOCH

Front cover design by Jacqueline Crawford
Front cover picture of Schiehallion from
the Standing Stone, Clach na h'Iobairte
© A. D. Cunningham, 1989

ISBN 0 905452 05 4

Published by
A. D. Cunningham
and
Perth and Kinross District Libraries
Shore Road
Perth, PH2 8BH

printed by
Cordfall Ltd
041 332 4640

CONTENTS

AUTHOR'S NOTE

I have enjoyed collecting the material for these stories over the last twenty years during which time I have been fortunate in being Expeditions Master at Rannoch School. This has enabled me to explore the hills and valleys of Rannoch, and to tramp the moors and the ancient tracks, visiting the deserted villages, the ruined crofts and the shielings of an area which was once full of people and their activities.

On these expeditions I have frequently been aided by the boys and girls of the school doing their explorations for their Duke of Edinburgh's Award. Other young participants in the Award Scheme journeying in the district have also contributed a great deal. Together they have helped me search out much information.

We have walked into the past, following a trail of legends and stories of Rannoch, where, according to James Robertson, writing about his childhood in the 1870's "there was no road or path leading anywhere in the district that was without its ghost". He and other children would listen with bated breath at ceilidhs as the adults told tales to one another of ghosts and witches, of the Evil Eye and other weird experiences.

People have told us their tales and we have explored the original places of these stories. We have talked to gamekeepers, shepherds and stalkers. We have questioned railwaymen, Hydro workers and foresters. We have listened to Youth Hostellers and gangrels from bothies; and fishermen who frequent Rannoch Moor have regaled us with accounts told them by their fathers and grandfathers. To all these I acknowledge my debt.

As a result of my previous book "A History of Rannoch", I have had many letters from people who have left the district, some from as far away as Canada, Australia, New Zealand and America, men and women whose ancestors lived at Rannoch, and they have provided helpful information and answers to many clues.

The stories have, of course, required much research, and I thank the Sandeman Library at Perth for their help. Speakers at the Local History Society and the members themselves have also contributed much to these tales. To all these sources I am very grateful, and particularly to Molly, my wife, for reading and commenting on the stories.

Rannoch 1989.

LEGENDS AND HISTORICAL TALES

1. THE STONE OF THE HEADS

St. Michael's Graveyard, Camghouran.

1. THE STONE OF THE HEADS

The original story of this event, as told by the old seanachaidh, the story teller, and handed down at ceilidhs, is related at such length and with so much detail that there is space only to give the bare outline of the tale, with some elaboration here and there to create atmosphere.

Many years ago a beautiful and well-favoured maiden called Marsali Macgregor who lived at Dunan in Rannoch was renowned far and wide for her commanding form and sweet nature. Many a young man sighed for her and she had plenty of suitors. One of these was a Mackintosh chief from Glen Loy who travelled all the way from Lochaber to Rannoch in the expectation of taking her back home as his wife. Although Marsali was impressed by his forceful manner and fine bearing she did not choose him. She had fallen in love with Ewan Cameron, a poor young farmer from Camghouran. When the Mackintosh learnt this he could not contain his anger. Not only was it a bitter disappointment to lose the desirable Marsali, but he found it particularly galling to be rejected in favour of a poor farmer, and a Cameron at that, for he had no love for this Clan. Their territory in Lochaber bordered on the Mackintosh country and they were continually at war with one another over land rights. He raged and cursed, and threatened vengeance on the pair of them.

However, Marsali and Ewan were soon wedded and they lived at Tigh na Dige beside the Black Wood. Here their years together were happy and carefree. Ewan worked hard on his farm which prospered, and Marsali raised a young family. They had long forgotten about Mackintosh and his threats, but he, on the other hand, still harboured resentment, a feeling that became more bitter over the years.

One day, on a return visit to his friends, the Macgregors, his jealousy was aroused anew when he heard how greatly respected Ewan had become, not only as a successful farmer but also as the outstanding huntsman of the Slios Garbh, he being known as Eoghain, sarshealgair an t-Sliosghairbh. Mackintosh's heart was full of envy and he became blind to all else but vengeance.

In this frame of mind he set off for Camghouran determined to kill Cameron and to abduct his wife. He and his followers arrived at the village to find it quiet. He stationed his men outside Tigh na Dige, and sword in hand, he burst through the door. Inside, Marsali, along with her children, was startled by this violent entry and hastily drew her children together to protect them. She recognised Mackintosh and saw by the wildness of his eyes that murder was in his heart.

"Where is he?" he yelled, striding around the cottage looking for Ewan. Marsali refused to speak, instead shaking her head and looking at him defiantly.

"Where is he?" he shouted once more, approaching her menacingly. She again said nothing although she was afraid that Ewan might return at any moment .

"Then I will take **YOU**," he cried, attempting to grasp her shoulder.

"Never," she cried, recoiling in horror. Angry at her reaction, and with mind inflamed with jealousy he grabbed one of the terrified children and said, "I will brain every one of your sons unless you submit."

"No," she said, "I will never do that." So he took the first one, then another, and then a third and he dashed their heads against a large stone. Before he could brain the fourth one, Marsali broke down and consented to go with him.

However, before he could carry her away, there were sounds of conflict outside. Ewan and the other men had returned from the fields and a fierce fight ensued. All the Mackintosh men were killed but Mackintosh himself who managed to escape. He fled along the lochside, closely pursued by Ewan and the villagers. Eventually he took refuge at Ardlarich and called on the protection of the Macgregors there. Ewan, mad with anger at the cowardly slaughter of his children, and bent on wreaking vengeance on their murderer, without pausing to make a plan, led a reckless attack on the house and he was killed as he crossed the threshold. His body was taken back to Camghouran and the band of villagers, saddened by his death returned, allowing the Mackintosh to slink away to Lochaber. Marsali was overcome by this further tragedy but she was comforted by Ewan's brother, William. He arranged for the graves to be dug, and after the burial ceremony he put his arms around Marsali's shoulders and said, "I will avenge the death of Ewan and his children," and he solemnly drew his dirk and kissed it. "I will go to Lochiel and enlist the help of the Camerons. They will bring restitution on the Mackintosh." He was inflamed with anger and determination, but

Marsali put her hand on his arm, saying, "No, let us have no more killing. Let us forget injuries and do good instead," she added, quoting the old Gaelic proverb, 'Mhuinntir chi math am muinntir eile, Is iadsa ni math do gach a cheile.'

Notwithstanding her pleas, William journeyed to Achnacarry, the home of Cameron of Lochiel, where the clan was being led by Taillear dubh na Tuaighe, the Tutor, because Lochiel was still a youth. The Tutor was a great warrior, famed for his skill with the mighty Lochaber Axe. He listened to William's request and agreed to help. Soon over a hundred fully armed warriors were gathered, all eagerly thirsting for a fight with their old enemies..

Meanwhile, Mackintosh after his escape from Ardlarich reached Loy where he secured himself in his castle which was heavily guarded. Here he felt safe, but he had moments of fear and times when he suffered remorse and melancholy. On one such night, in a low state of depression and guilt he retired to bed. At midnight he was startled to see the ghost of Ewan Cameron with head all bloody. He cowered in terror as the apparition pointed at him, and said, "O Mackintosh, the murderer of my children, tonight you will suffer." (Mhicantoisich mhort mo phaisdean, bios tu 'nochd ad thruaghan grannda). Although brave enough in battle, Mackintosh fled in fear from the ghost. He made for the battlements. But here he suffered a worse shock for his castle was surrounded and the night was full of the noise of battle. He heard the shrieks of his dying warriors as the Lochaber axes of the Camerons cut them down. Soon all were killed and the castle was burnt to the ground. All the neighbouring Mackintosh habitations were also put to flame, after which William and the Camerons left, taking with them a hugh creach of cattle, driving them back to Rannoch.

Their vengeance was not complete for they had to deal with the Macgregors of Ardlarich for their part in the death of Ewan. However, when they arrived there the house was deserted and they learnt that they had flown to Crossmount so they set off after them. As they approached the Macgregor's position they were surprised to see Marsali hurrying towards them. Breathlessly she exhorted the Camerons to show mercy to the fugitives. "They are Macgregors, my own people," she said. "Spare them", she begged. "I forgive them for murdering my husband." — Ged bhrist mo chairdean fhein mo chrid, tha mis' toirt dhoibhsan uile sith — "Though my own friends broke my heart, my peace to each of them I give."

Meanwhile, Ardlarich, peering from the cave in which he was hiding, saw with increasing dread, the powerful force of Camerons, their swords and mighty axes flashing in the sun. Because of his fear and the hopelessness of his situation he decided his best chance lay in immediate escape. So he rushed forth from the cave, sped down the hillside and made an enormous leap on to a boulder in the river and reached the other side. The Camerons hesitated, then respecting Marsali's wishes, allowed him to scramble away to safety.

NOTES

1. Marsali lived to a great old age, revered by all, and was buried in the graveyard where the rest of her family were laid to rest. It is usually called the Cameron Cemetery or more properly St. Michael's.
2. The stone on which the children were put to death was placed at the entrance of the graveyard and has ever since been called Clach na Ceann, The Stone of the Heads. It is the one at the left hand side of the gate as you face it.
3. Tigh na Dige, the House of the Mound was probably on the same knoll as the graveyard.
4. Iain Biorach, the fourth son who was saved by his mother, probably grew up to be the Iain Cameron of West Camghouran who was the largest farmer in the district. In 1778 he had nearly 400 beasts made up of 8 horses, 36 cows and 350 sheep, most of them presumably being the herds taken from the raid on the Mackintoshes.
5. Local readers are probably familiar with the short version of this story by Alexander Cameron in his fine book *A Highland Parish* in which the incident which led to the killing of the children was caused by a dispute over the purchase of arrows at Perth.
6. The boulder at the place called Macgregor's Leap can no longer be seen because the hydro-electric schemes have flooded the river.
7. The old cave on Crossmount called Macgregor's Cave has now been turned into a summer house but steps lead up to a cleft in the rocks to the look-out point from where Ardlarich first saw the Camerons approaching.

2. MACGREGOR THE BOLD

Eilean nam Faoileag.
(This and the other island were used as
strongholds by the MacGregors.)

2. MACGREGOR THE BOLD

The man ran, foam round his mouth, sweat from his brow and blood at his nostrils. He was still swift but he was near the limit of his strength.

Scrambling over the debris of rocks he headed for the narrow pass ahead where he would make a last fight for it. The black dog was close to him, and behind the dog was a pack of hounds and then a dozen figures on foam flecked horses.

Young Duncan MacGregor had been driven from his home at Ardchoille by the Campbells and he had been hunted for four days. They nearly caught him in Glen Dochart but he avoided pursuit by taking to the hill burn. In Glen Lochay he had been given food and shelter, near the heart of the Campbell country of Glen Lyon, but now, in sight of Rannoch, his enemies were nearly on him.

Lungs at bursting point he reached the gap in the hills at Lairig a' Mhuic. He turned, dagger drawn, determined to fight to the last. The black dog was only yards away, when, from behind a rock, a warrior seized the dog, then a group of men were among the hounds slashing with swords, and a further band flung themselves at the horses, pulling them down and unseating their riders.

There was a confusion of sounds, cries of pain from the wounded and yells of triumph from the warriors, but it was soon over. The Campbells and their dogs were driven off, leaving their horses behind. It soon became obvious to Duncan that the warrior band had taken the opportunity of his plight to ambush his pursuers for their horses and not to save him, but he was nevertheless grateful to them.

He was glad to join his rescuers as they made their way to the Black Wood of Rannoch. He learnt that they were a band of MacGregors who, like himself, had been driven from their homes by the Campbells. Each was living the life of an outlaw, 'fear so shean f'on choille', or 'the man whose head is under the wood' as they were called. As he travelled with them he recalled to himself his anger and the incidents which had led to his present predicament.

Duncan had expected to become Chief of the MacGregor Clan on the death of John MacGregor of Glen Orchy but he was cheated out of this by Sir Duncan Campbell. Sir Duncan produced a Royal Proclamation ratifying his claim which he had wheedled out of a badly advised young King James IV. MacGregor, who was a hot-headed youth of 18, disputed the claim but instead of being discreet and attempting litigation he behaved in a wild and foolhardy fashion. He undertook a one-man guerrilla warfare of mayhem and murder against all Campbells and their property.

His violence, robbery and arson instilled terror amongst them. Soon every Campbell was after his blood. They drove him out of Archoille and they formed bands of vigilantes to track him down. With so many enemies against him he had to flee for his life, and as Rannoch was noted for harbouring broken men and fugitives from justice he headed for the sanctuary of its hills and forests.

Duncan was a dashing figure and his singular hatred of the Campbells, and his determination to win back his inheritance by the sword made him a natural leader of the MacGregor outlaws in Rannoch. He recruited all the other broken men in the district (even giving them the name of MacGregor) and welded them into fighting units which became renowned for their daring throughout the countryside. To those MacGregors who, like him, had lost their lands or their birthright, he gave hope and something to live and fight for.

In order to survive, the MacGregor bands had to thieve and plunder, and although their chief targets were the Campbells, many other people in the countryside suffered. In spite of this, Duncan acquired a reputation as an heroic figure and many young MacGregors joined his "Children of the Mist", as they were romantically called. Because of his ambitious and daring exploits against the Campbells he was given the name Ladasach or "The Bold". But like other brave and adventurous men, he underestimated the cunning of his chief adversary, Sir Duncan Campbell of Glen Orchy.

This led to his undoing. It was after a successful raid into far Glen Orchy when Ladasach and his "Children of the Mist" were driving home a large head of cattle stolen from the Campbells. It was slow progress with so many beasts and they were delayed even further by the rivers being in spate. However, as they neared Rannoch, although weary after their long journey, they were elated with their success. But their shouts of jubilation were silenced at the sight that met them. Houses had been destroyed, flocks and herds taken and people wounded or slaughtered. His enemy Sir Duncan had swooped on Rannoch in his absence, destroying the Island fortress and the houses in the Blackwood, and as a final insult he had hanged one of his warriors. Ladasach saw the body swinging from a tree and was shocked to find that the pitiful figure was that of his trusty lieutenant. Overcoming his anger he looked at the corpse and addressed it sadly, saying, "Alastair, my friend, you have nothing to take to heaven with you. When I go, I too will have nothing, unless", he added, looking at the captured cattle, "they are short of cows up there".

To overcome his feeling of sorrow he immediately prepared to retaliate. Within hours he was riding over the hills with some chosen warriors, fully armed and bent on revenge. But he did not take account again of his wily opponent. All the passes to Rannoch were guarded, and Ladasach and his men rode into a trap. The battle that ensued was one-sided. The MacGregors, taken by surprise, were routed, Ladasach's horse was brought to the ground and he was captured.

Sir Duncan had him chained and thrown into the beheading pit at Balloch. However, luck was on Ladasach's side because before he could be executed Sir Duncan was "called-up" and in the Battle of Flodden was killed. In the confusion that followed, Ladashach's friends were able to free him, and he soon resumed his vendetta against the Campbells; this time his adversary was Sir Colin Campbell of Glen Orchy, the son of the man who had captured him. His cattle were stolen, his houses destroyed and his tenants terrified but Sir Colin was not intimidated. He continued the Campbell technique of acquiring the land and possessions of MacGregors by evicting or bribing them, and he swore to hound Ladasach to the death.

One day he visited his son Archibald Campbell of Innerwick, in Glen Lyon to co-ordinate plans for attacks and preparations for defence against Ladasach and his outlaws. Ladasach received word that he was to be there and he saw the opportunity of capturing all the Glen Orchy dynasty and putting a stop to the Campbell perfidy once and for all.

As he approached Glen Lyon that night, the trees stirred and rustled as Ladasach kept the band of horsemen in the shadows, silent except for the occasional snort of a horse and the clink of a sword and harness. Archibald Campbell's house was silhouetted in the moonlight as Ladasach halted his force. In whispers he gave the final orders. One party was to secure the enemies' horses in the stables and the main force was to attack the castle.

As the MacGregors moved into the courtyard the silence was broken as charging warriors were amongst them. They had ridden into an ambush. Men and horses tangled in the confusion of the darkness. There were cries of men and shrieks of horses. Ladasach rallied his men with the clan's war cry "Gregarach" but there was nothing for it but to retreat. He got his men clear of the house but as he was directing them over the bridge it collapsed. Horses floundered in the mud and the Campbells fell on them again. Ladasach was a saddened man as he rode back to Rannoch with the remnants of his party; sad at the loss of many good warriors and sad that there was a spy in his camp.

Sir Colin, pleased with his victory, sought further success against Ladasach by "persuading" peaceful MacGregors, by threats and bribery, to join him and renounce Ladasach as leader of the Clan. When Ladasach heard that the respected Alasdair Odhar MacGregor had become a "turn-coat" he was very angry. That night he and his son stealthily made their way to Glen Lyon, they swam the river to avoid the Campbell patrols and at dawn reached Morenish on Loch Tay. They broke into the house, dragged the unfortunate Alasdair outside and murdered him.

Sir Colin was furious at Ladasach's action and he immediately obtained a Royal Warrant for his head, and with this he called on all the neighbouring clans, the Stewarts, the Robertsons, the Drummonds, the Campbells and others to form an alliance to help to bring "the foul murderers" to justice . . . and "to pursue to the death Duncan Ladasach MacGregor and his son". Ladasach, surrounded by enemies, with odds heavily against him, now showed his remarkable character. Undaunted by the "big battalions" he swept into their strongholds, time after time and day after day without respite. He chased them, harried them from hill to hill and terrorised their followers. No one could stand against him. He finally put paid to their alliance with the Campbells by riding deep into the Robertson country. Showing no fear for this mighty clan, he burned down their house at Strathbaan and exacted a heavy toll on their warriors. The audacity of the MacGregor outlaws and their leader's courage made a deep impression upon the generation in which he lived. Their actions caused Campbell's 'friends', understandably to withdraw their support. So Sir Colin realised he must find other methods to beat his hated enemy.

He decided on reconciliation. Perhaps Ladasach would listen to reason. So he drew up an agreement declaring that he forgave "Duncane and Gregour (his son), servants and followers". He pardoned them all fully, and offered terms of amity and peace. He proposed a conference at the Castle of Balloch (Kenmore) with a certain number of friends on both sides to settle the dispute and to ratify future friendship. Of course he planned to capture Ladasach and his followers when off their guard.

Ladasach appeared to trust the agreement for he set off as agreed with only a few trusty men. All went well. No one attempted to hinder their progress through Glen Lyon. They were surmounting Drummond Hill in sight of the Castle of Balloch when they encountered an old man – he was by a large grey stone – praying. Struck with a thing so unusual, Ladasach, drawing near, discovered the old man praying for the dead. He seemed to be addressing the stone, and amongst his prayers he repeated the following sentences over and over again. "Oh stone, beware! When the black bull's head appears, MacGregor's sword will not save his head. Deep the dungeon – sharp the axe – and short the shrift".

Lasasach realised that this was meant for him as a warning. The old man had taken this round about way of telling him of the conspiracy, for fear of Sir Colin and being sworn to secrecy. The MacGregors discussed what action to take, and they contiunued on their way. When they arrived at Balloch they were received with every appearance of kindness. Sir Colin and Ladasach discussed their differences in a friendly fashion and then they were all invited for dinner in the great hall, each Campbell having a MacGregor on his right hand. The meal started and all went well, both sides being polite to one another. Then the black bull's head was brought in. As soon as it appeared, before the Campbells could make a move, the MacGregors had their daggers out and held them against each Campbell throat. Armed retainers were not able to help for fear of their chief losing his life.

The MacGregors carried off Sir Colin and his men and dragged them to the top of Drummond Hill. Ladasach was sorely tempted to take the life of his enemy but instead he forced him to subscribe an ample pardon and remission for all past injuries and a promise of future friendship. Sir Colin was made to swear on his dirk that he would keep to his word.

So Ladasach returned with his signed agreement. Like a politician of more recent times returning from the Munich crisis, so Ladasach entered Rannoch assuring his waiting outlaws that he had gained "peace in our time". Alas for the words of leaders! A few days later, while on a peaceful mission with his two sons to Fortingall, he was captured by Sir Colin's men, and he was executed in unholy haste on 16th June, 1552, with his sons, Gregor and Malcolm.

3. SARAH'S SECOND SIGHT

Sarah was buried with the rest of her family in the MacGregor Graveyard
at Killichonan, where the old Celtic Church of St Conan stood.
The old font is the only part of the original church still remaining.

3. SARAH'S SECOND SIGHT

Rannoch has been famous from olden times for the numbers of persons having the gift of second sight (or da shealladh), the fascinating borderland between the seen and the unseen world. It is little less than a hundred years ago that the last anecdotes of second sight were recorded in Rannoch. One of its inhabitants, Sarah, was well known in the village. She lived with her husband and a large family in a small slated cottage near the burn, close to the graveyard. She was a kind creature who lead a righteous life adhering to Christian principles, wishing no harm to anyone and she was always glad when she was able to help people.

One evening at dusk she was chatting as usual to her neighbours. All were about to disperse to prepare the evening meal for their menfolk when Sarah gave a loud exclamation. She could see a funeral procession approaching up the road. She told the other wives who looked in the direction she indicated. Although it was nearly dark there was sufficient light for them to see that there was nothing there.

"You must be mistaken", they said, "their is nothing to be seen".

"Yes, said Sarah. "Look, it is going into the end house".

"No, said the neighbours, "the road is deserted". They looked askance at Sarah, all of them greatly ill at ease.

Sarah was watching the house; it was the home of her particular friend. She continued staring, eyelids wide, when the onlookers saw her recoil and a look of horror appear on her face. She was seeing the apparition of her friend dressed in death-clothes being carried by the funeral party to the graveyard. In no time at all she could hear the pick and spade of the phantom gravedigger. The neighbours by this time were terrified by her disclosures, and although they had not seen or heard anything unusual they were greatly affected by her demeanor. However, taking courage from their numbers they all went to the end cottage. They found the occupant sitting in the chair, dead.

Not long after this there was another incident, as a result of which Sarah was so badly affected that she became ill. She was reluctant to talk about it but what occurred soon became well-known. She had seen a visionary contest in the graveyard. It was a furious battle between good and evil angels for the soul of a well-known villager who was on the point of death. Then she saw rehearsals of the funeral itself. She could recognise the taishs (phantoms) of living friends and relations going for the wood to make the coffin and collecting the nails and the grave clothes. Soon came the sounds of the coffin being made. She heard the hammerings and workings of the plane in the dark workshop of the carpenter. A few days later the person died and the very people that she had seen in her vision were performing the same actions as the phantoms had done.

These incidents in which she was able to see things that were to happen in the future invested Sarah with mystery and awe, but it was her ability to 'see' things that had happened in the past that brought her into the eyes of a wider public.

A person in Kinloch Rannoch had disappeared suddenly, and inquiries and searches were made for many days without success. At length some one suggested that Sarah should be consulted. She agreed to help the relatives but is was not an experience that she enjoyed for she saw in her vision a scene of tragedy. She saw a man dripping with water. She suffered the agony of the victim as his lungs filled with pain and she saw the body rolling and swaying in the underwater currents. When her composure returned she expressed sorrow to the relatives but she indicated exactly what the scene looked like where the body was. Sure enough the villagers recognised the description of the place and there they found the drowned person.

There were two or three other occasions when she was consulted and she was able to picture the scenes and indicate where to find the bodies of the unfortunate victims. However, there was one occasion when she was aware of a tragedy before the people arrived to ask for help. She saw in her mind a crowd of people hurrying over the hills from the West and she knew she was needed. She knew why they had come and she was able to picture the scene that had caused them to seek her. This is what she saw.

She was looking at a loch in a part of the country she had never seen before. It was wild weather and no day for fishing for the sky was thick with clouds scudding before a threatening wind. The solitary boat was bobbing and pitching as the gale howled up from the west. Before the fisherman could reach the shelter of the shore the boat capsized and the man was dragged under. His fight for life was brief. Sarah sensed his mind darkening as the cold waters of death claimed him. All this was very real to her and she was able to describe the stretch of sand

and the clutter of boulders that ringed a small depression in the shore line where his body had come to rest. The relatives of the fisherman had come from Loch Awe where the tragedy had occurred. They had dragged the loch but because they had not been able to find the body they had come to ask Sarah's help. Now they went back and were able to locate the place described by her, and there they found it.

Because of these unusual successes her reputation spread far and wide. It even reached the ears of someone in London. As a result, one day in 1895 she was visited by Lord Bute who was Vice-President of the Psychical Research Society who took a note of all her experiences. She told him that she did not look upon her gift of second sight as enviable or desirable; in fact, although she expressed a regret that she had such a gift, she took comfort from the fact that the bible contained instances of many worthy people having apparitions. He congratulated her for not using her faculties for evil purposes and he assured her that she should be proud of possessing a precious age old gift from her Celtic ancestors.

(Rev. J. Sinclair who reported these incidents at the time gave her the name, Sarah, concealing her real name to spare her family from any unwanted publicity.)

4. THE GREAT EVANGELIST

The monument in the village square erected to the memory of
'Dugald Buchanan, Evangelist and Sacred Poet,
died 2nd June, 1763'.

4. THE GREAT EVANGELIST

Dugald Buchanan was "a teacher
Of truth, and a preacher
With a message of mercy to tell
With an arm swift and strong
To pull back the throng,
That headlong were plunging to hell."

It was a Sunday and the sun had risen over Schiehallion when Dugald Buchanan mounted his horse and rode westwards along the lochside. Although the young evangelist had a friendly word for everyone he passed, his mind was occupied with the object of his journey. Today for the first time he was visiting the Braes of Rannoch, a wild and lawless country of freebooters and rievers situated at the west end of the loch.

He had come to Rannoch in 1751 when wicked men ruled the district and poverty and despair were everywhere. He visited every home in Kinloch Rannoch and the neighbouring villages, bringing hope and comfort to the needy. He taught the people trades and sensible agriculture so that prosperity resulted. He was loved by young and old. The young he taught in his school and the old flocked to hear him preach at Ballinloan and Kinloch. The open air was his Church and his message was simple: 'Love God and love one another'. So great was his influence that the people became respected and law-abiding citizens. Would he be able to do the same for the Braes?

As he led his horse through the birches he wondered how he would fare with the Muinntir a' Bhraigh (Folk of the Braes) for their reputation for savagery and lawlessness was known throughout the country. Living there were fugitives and broken men from different clans. Hundreds of wild MacGregor robbers lived side by side with Menzies men on Slios Min. These men carried on a bitter feud with the Robertsons of the South side (The Slios Garbh) and the Camerons.

He could hear the murmur of a multitude as he reached Kenachlacher. Hundreds had gathered to hear the preacher. He suspected that many of them were there with the aim of settling scores with their opponents. As he approached the river he could hear the loud shouting; the curses and threats that were being hurled across the river by the rival clansmen.

He paused for a long moment. Then fearlessly urging his horse forward he splashed into the river and rode between the banks that were crowded with wild looking men. Reining his mount he swung round so that he was facing them. The noise ceased. The atmosphere was electric.

Dugald's eyes flashed as he saw that each man had a weapon of some sort.

"Cast your arms down," he commanded. "Put your weapons down," he shouted even louder, "This is my Church. Let there be peace here."

There were sullen murmuring. "We have a blood feud. They are our enemies," the opponents on each bank shouted.

"I have come here to talk of peace, not of fighting," said Dugald. The muttering stopped. His manner commanded attention. Some put their weapons down. He waited . The men were now utterly quiet.

"Some of you are shedders of blood," he said, "lifters of cattle and lawless robbers. You take part in feuds and bloody fighting. There is robbery here and violence. There is no love. No charity." He spoke quietly, his eyes softening.

"You are sinful people but you can repent. All can be forgiven. You men are brave and courageous in battle. You are skilful in 'spreach' but your motives are evil and self-seeking. Who amongst you is brave and courageous enough to join my band of honest men of God?" He continued his sermon, upbraiding them for their sins and exhorting them to repentance.

"Over the river bank," he said, "are men like you. They are your brothers. Feuds do not exist between people of charity. Forgive your enemy. Devote your energies to friendliness and kind deeds, not sinfulness. Step into the river and greet one another!"

As he finished speaking there was a great sigh from the multitude. First one, then another plunged into the river to offer friendship with those on the other side. MacGregors embraced Camerons, Menzies and Robertsons came together as friends. The feud was broken . . . for ever.

The Braes, like the rest of Rannoch, settled down to husbandry and peaceful pursuits and Dugald continued his good work helping all the people. He preached regularly at Foss, Rannoch and the Braes but, unfortunately, in 1768 like hundreds more in the district, he died of the plague. People of later generations, remembering the outstanding achievements of the great evangelist in bringing peace and prosperity to the valley, erected in his honour a monument in the square of Kinloch Rannoch.

(The verse of poetry quoted is from Dugald Buchanan's poem 'the Skull'. . The person who is the subject of this verse is imaginary, although like Dugald in every way)

5. THE BROKEN HEART STONE

The Broken Heart Stone.

5. THE BROKEN HEART STONE

The original Heart Stone was of Perthshire granite and the story of it goes back to the days when the Road to the Isles was just a foot-track through the heather from Rannoch to Fort William and then on to the Western Isles. As the track reached Loch Eigheach it passed a huge boulder called the Heart Stone which from olden times had provided both rest and shelter for the weary travellers journeying from the Islands to Rannoch or beyond to the trysts at Falkirk.

When at last a road of sorts was constructed over the moor it followed the old track and when the first road makers came to the Heart Stone they found it partly in the way. They had not any heavy gear to move it and they did not like the idea of swinging the road round it. So they bored and plugged and nearly split it in half to the great dismay of the Rannoch people. Then it became known as the Broken Heart Stone.

There it rested by the old road, a prominent landmark to the travellers, known to the Highlanders in all parts of the world, a milestone on their road to home. Then came the new project of the North of Scotland Hydro Electric Board – the Gaur Scheme.

In the fifties the workmen poured into this isolated area and began to build a dam across the Gaur burn. When the people of Rannoch realised that the Broken Heart was going to be submerged by the new reservoir at Loch Eigheach there was an outcry. Letters poured in from all quarters all with the same request, "Save the Broken Heart". Important members of the Community approached the contractors on the job and they moved the Broken Heart Stone to safety to an appropriate site near where the old road from Corrour crosses the new road to Rannoch Station.

The motor crane just managed to move the 15 tons stone so that modern travellers from the Isles are still able to rest by the stone that has for long stood by the Road to the Isles, just as their forbears did.

6. DUNCAN THE FAT

Leum Donnachadh Reamhar
The Leap of Duncan the Fat.

The Old Apple Tree.

Loch Con.

6. THE EXPLOITS OF DUNCAN THE FAT

One of the early heroes of Rannoch was Donnachaidh Reamhair or Duncan the Fat about whom many historical and traditional accounts have been told. His hunting exploits, his cattle raids and his frequent battles with his neighbours equipped him well for his warlike adventures and in support of his friend Robert Bruce.

One day one of Duncan's clansmen arrived at his castle, bloodied and exhausted, to report that a large force led by MacDougal of Lorn, a hated opponent of Bruce, was approaching Rannoch from the North. Breathlessly he described how he managed to escape with his life when they stormed his village. His last sight as he fled was of his own house going up in flames.

Duncan questioned the messenger for other details and then issued orders for his warriors to be assembled at Camus-Ericht. Meanwhile he had to find out more information about the enemy so he dressed himself as a travelling packman, a fairly good disguise for those days for such men were frequent visitors to lonely glens. He made his way up the river Ericht until he came to their camp.

He was able to move amongst the men peddling his wares, eyes hooded but observing the preparations for battle. Through the crowded camp he went amongst groups of soldiers, some busy with equipment, others resting on the ground, past the tethered horses, to the Chiefs standard. There the tall figure of MacDougal of Lorn, pale of face and smiling, was telling his warriors the sort of jokes that soldiers love.

The leader, in the midst of one of his stories, noticed the pedlar. There was something about his bearing and his young appearance that aroused his suspicions. "Come here, my man," he said.

Duncan, realising the danger, shouldered his pack and started moving away.

"Here! Stop that man," cried MacDougal as Duncan started to run. A man attempted to stop him but Duncan pushed him aside and increased speed. He cast away his pack and made for the river. Others were now following him but he reached the riverside ahead of the pursuit. There he hesitated. The river was in full spate and rocky. One of MacDougal's men, faster than the others, was nearly upon him and Duncan had to do something. He looked again at the river. On either side were steep rocks, rising perpendicular from the water, and about sixteen feet apart. Between the rocks the water roared with great velocity, throwing the foam and spray high in the air. In desperation he ran the few yards to the edge, leapt with all his might and cleared the chasm. He landed safely on the opposite bank. He picked himself up and saw the pursuers hesitating. Unwilling to emulate his feat they turned away thwarted and angry, and returned to their camp.

THE BATTLE OF THE RED CORRIE: Duncan meanwhile made his way to meet his men at the place arranged, Camus-Ericht. He had already decided on his plan and he explained this to his warriors. They were to move immediately, with the utmost silence, into positions around Coire Earra Dheargan, the Red Corrie, ready to ambush MacDougal's forces as they came down from the hills.

Early next morning the enemy approached. As the sun rose above Schiehallion casting light on the quiet villages of Slion Min the peace was suddenly shattered by the cries of Duncan's men as they sprang from behind rocks and from the heather. The surprise was complete for the enemy were driven into the corrie. Here, amidst the confusion, MacDougal was attempting to assemble his forces when, from the hills above the corrie, swept the rest of Duncan's men causing the enemy to scatter. Rain had fallen during the night and the floor of the corrie was boggy and heavy so that men and horses squelched and tangled in a wilderness of broken bodies. Above the clash of weapons arose the battle cries of men and the shrieks of the wounded as both sets of warriors fought.

MacDougal's men never recovered from the surprise attack and they finally broke away and scrambled up the hillside leaving their dead behind them on the reddened earth. Quiet fell over the battlefield except for the moans of the injured and the raucous crying of the gulls overhead. Duncan, exhausted but triumphant, walked among the bodies. Lying near a rock was the still figure of MacDougal who at first sight appeared to be dead, but he was unconscious. He had received a severe blow on the head which had knocked him out. When he recovered, though still very dazed, he was led away as a captive.

MACDOUGAL'S ESCAPE FROM THE ISLAND: Duncan planned to hold MacDougal prisoner until he received a ransom for his release. So he had him taken to his island keep in Loch Rannoch, Eilean nam Faoileag. Here, MacDougal, though still weak, examined his prison carefully, looking for some means of escape. Although it was a small tower, only three of four paces to either wall, it was strongly built. The walls were thick;the door sturdy and the windows mere slits. Even if he could break out, MacDougal realised that it was far too far for him to swim. As he was looking through the windows he saw a boat approaching. It was two jailors bringing him food so he hurried to his corner of the cell.

Cautiously they entered. They were reassured when they saw the prisoner lying down, obviously still suffering from his wounds. They placed the food for him against the wall. It was sufficient for a few days and included amongst it a sack of apples. As one of the guards was lifting this, MacDougal saw his chance. He sprang at him, pushing him so hard that he stumbled and lurched against his companion who crashed into the wall. They both fell to the ground and the apples were scattered everywhere. As they attempted to gather the apples and gain their feet at the same time MacDougal was able to open the door, escape and lock it behind him.

He took their boat and rowed with all his might to the Slios Garbh, knowing that Duncan and his troops still occupied the north shore. He was able to land safely and avoid capture by taking to the hills until it was safe to join his own men again.

The rock where he landed is still called MacDougal's Rock and the hillside above, where he made his escape, is Creagan Mhic Dhughaill. Also the very ancient apple tree, now gnarled and hoary, standing by the roadside, less than half a mile from Finnart Lodge, is still associated with this old story.

BURIED ALIVE: Although lauded in local tales for his heroic exploits, Duncan the Fat can claim no glory from this final story for it tells how he buried his wife alive. The scene where Duncan perpetrated this cruel crime was at Loch Con, a lonely loch in the Errochty hills five or six miles due north of Rannoch.

He was renowned for his courage and success in battle. Not only had he defeated two armies which invaded Rannoch during the Wars of Independence but he had fought side by side with Robert Bruce at Bannockburn, bringing great honour to his clan by his bravery. When not engaged in these battles, like many of his fellows, he led a life of 'hame-sucken' and cattle thieving against neighbouring clans.

During these years he married a wealthy maid from Lennox. By all accounts she was beautiful and she provided him with a daughter and a comfortable home. In those early years when he returned from his various forays they would enjoy spending long summer days together at her favourite place, Loch Con. But their relationship gradually changed; their summer visits became less frequent and he grew tired of her. Whether is was because she was unable to give him a son or whether it was that he had met a neighbouring heiress is not clear, but he was determined to get rid of her. To get rid of her at once and for ever he chose the island cave of Loch Con as a suitable place to carry out this savage deed. Secretly he made his preparations.

When all was ready he went to his wife and asked her if she would like to go to Loch Con again for he had a surprise for her. "I have made a grotto out of the island cave, suitable for my lady." he said. Unaware of his evil intentions and thinking this indicated an improvement in their relations, she eagerly agreed.

It is easy to imagine her eyes shining with joy as he rowed her the short distance to the wooded island. Birds fluttered away as they landed and led her to the cave. It was dark inside and her smile changed to a look of dismay as he seized her and tied her to a stake. Fear and anguish beset her as she realised what he was doing for he was pulling stones across the entrance, stones that were separating her from life and liberty. Soon the barrier of the entrance was a barrier thicker than a prison wall and the sun's rays were obliterated. He continued piling stones over the entrance so that her cries could no longer be heard.

Duncan obviously felt no remorse at her slow death. While he enjoyed the warmth of the sun and the heather in bloom, and the grotto became a charnel house, he was soon wooing the daughter of the Chieftain of Glen Tilt. The father's suspicions that his wife was still alive were allayed by Duncan, for he was able to say with his hand on his dirk "No, I have no wife above the ground."

Accounts tell us that Duncan's new wife presented him with two sons who eventually were to be the pro-genitors of the Robertson Clan but Duncan did not live a life of complete ease for it is said that he was haunted by the ghost of his former wife, 'a rail-thin woman, her face white, her hair streaming, and her eyes blood-red with weeping.' There are other versions of this story which tell of his wife being imprisoned and being released later.

Whichever story the reader accepts it must be agreed that neither event is worthy of one of Rannoch's better known heroes.

7. THE BLACKWOOD STORY

Mullinvadie
(The Mill of the Wolf).

Tign Na Coille.

7. THE BLACKWOOD STORY

The ancient Blackwood (Coille Dubh) of Rannoch, the famous remnant of the old Caledonian Forest, is a perpetual source of pride to the inhabitants of Rannoch. Here this grandeur of Nature is their heritage. In Innischalden and the western half of the wood the pines are short, heavy branched trees, magnificent in their ruggedness, differing from those in the eastern half, near Dall, where there are tall spire-like trunks, elegant and powerful, the whole wood reminding visitors of what Rannoch, and indeed what much of Scotland was like in years gone by when vast tracts of the country were covered in trees. But the inhabitants were not always careful guardians; for they came near to destroying the Blackwood on many occasions.

In the old days the Blackwood's remoteness and trackless cover gave protection and security to hundreds of robbers and freebooters who ranged far and wide plundering property, stealing cattle and extracting black-meal (black mail) from frightened inhabitants. To get rid of these men the woods were frequently set alight. Such fires raged for days or weeks at a time and thousands of trees were lost.

Also when wolves roamed the land the woods provided shelter for these creatures and so the inhabitants set fire to the trees in order to burn them out. On one occasion, at the beginning of the 18th Century there was one wolf left in Rannoch which continually evaded capture. A large scale hunt was organised and eventually the wolf was forced to take refuge in the Blackwood. So the people did not hesitate to set the wood alight. As the fire spread the wolf was driven further and further towards the edge of the trees. Finally it dashed from the flames, avoided its attackers and leapt into the water. The astonished people watched it swimming across the loch.

It landed on the north shore and made for Ben a Chuallaich and the safety of the mountain. But passing close to Miller Robertson's house it scented the aroma of baking from the kitchen. Emboldened and ravenous from hunger it pushed through the door which was ajar. Stalking in unseen it saw a cradle in the corner in which there was a six month's baby. It was just preparing to drag the child out when the wife turned from the table where she was making potato scones. She was horrified when she saw the wolf but without any hesitation she went to the defence of her baby. She had a potato masher in her hand and she brought this down on the wolfs head with all her might. The wolf fell dead at her feet. To celebrate this brave deed and the death of the troublesome wolf, the Robertson Clan Chief called the house thereafter Mullinvadie, the Mill of the Wolf.

Though decimated by these fires to rid the wood of robbers and wolves and by many accidental fires, the Blackwood nevertheless survived. But in 1784 the whole of the wood was under threat of complete destruction, not by fire but by the axe. Every tree was to be cut down! The wood was sold to a public company who agreed to pay two and fourpence for each tree they felled. Soon every person in Rannoch was employed in the wood, and it was a godsend! Yes, the people were grateful, for they were close to starvation after a series of bad harvests.

The Company had devised a skilful scheme in which the felled trees were transported along a series of canals built along the hillside. They were projected down shoots to hurtle down to the loch a mile below. Here they were lashed together in rafts and floated down by loch and river to Dundee. Fortunately for the future of the Blackwood the project proved uprofitable and was abandoned, but it lasted long enough for the people to survive the emergency.

After the noise and bustle of the logging project the Blackwood became peaceful again. It was inhabited by a few men involved in iron smelting, others in small wood industries, and there were still those who preferred to exist outside the law and live 'under the wood'. It was while purchasing some wood in the Blackwood with his father that young Duncan MacAra encountered some of these men. He had wandered away by himself while his father was bargaining and measuring wood with the timber merchant when he was suddenly attacked. He tussled with his opponents but he was soon overpowered and robbed of his boots. He hobbled back to his father mortified and particularly angry because his boots were new ones.

A few years later when he was the Rev. Duncan MacAra of Fortingall and responsible for visiting the Mainntir a' Braigh (Folk of the Braes) he was passing the Blackwood when he was set upon again. The men pulled him from his saddle, hauled him into the wood and compelled him to baptise a child, which he did under protest. When they let him go he was furious. However he got his own back. Remembering the unhappy loss of his new boots and this further indignity, he brought the wrath of God to bear on the unfortunate inhabitant of Blackwood. It was not known exactly what threats he used but the miserable offender had to appear for 26 successive sabbaths to do penance in front of the congregation at Fortingall, a distance of over 20 miles. Lets hope his boots stood up to it!

Whenever the Minister made his way up the loch to Catechise the people of the Braes his progress was reported step by step by 'look outs' so that the respectable people could dust their bibles and the good wife could get out her clean white subag before he arrived. This efficient intelligence organisation was also used when the 'gaugers' (excisemen) came so that the shebeen or Poit Dhubh (Illicit Still) was able to be hidden in good time. Because of its remoteness the Blackwood was ideal for distilling a good drappie and people were rarely caught. An additional precaution taken was to call on the help of the fairies. Whenever the illicit whisky was 'ready ', the distiller would always put out the first portion in a saucer for the fairies who would then use their magic powers to protect this illegal activity.

However, in 1850 or thereabouts, there was an old smuggler who failed to call on their magic. He lived at Tummel Bridge and he used to distil his whisky in the Blackwood. His custom was to travel by horse and cart and spend most of the night at his still. He had distilled for many years and he had become confident and careless. On one occasion he was told that the gaugers were about, but he did not take heed. He calmly finished his distilling for the day. Alas, he did not leave a saucer for the fairies, and sure enough, before he could hitch his horse to the cart the gaugers had captured him. He was put in prison where, unfortunately he died while serving his sentence.

Although the illicit distillers believed in the magic of the fairies that inhabit the Blackwood there was a hunter who encountered a magic of quite a different sort. He lived at Tigh na Coille on the edge of the Blackwood and he was out one day stalking a deer. Like all experienced hunters he was moving silently when he spotted his quarry. He was able to get in range and was surprised to find it was a hind and her calf. It was unusual to find a hind and a calf together at that particular time. Normally he would not have shot her but times were hard and the larder was empty. As he raised the gun and sighted his eye along the barrel the hind and calf mysteriously changed into a young woman and a child. Appalled at the narrow escape he had from shooting one whom he recognised as an intimate acquaintance of his own, he lowered the gun.

Wiping the cold sweat from his brow he looked again, and there was the hind gazing at him mournfully with the calf snuggling close to her side. Realising that he was in the presence of something supernatural he was seized with panic, and he bolted headlong for home. He glanced back once but it was enough to show him the hind and the calf bounding gracefully after him over the breast-high heather, and gaining on him. In terror he sped on, heart pounding and black shadows floating before his eyes, until he could not take another step. He had run himself to a standstill, so he turned in desperation with his back to a tree. He called loudly for help but he was alone in the wood. For a moment he thought they had disappeared but there was a flash of movement and the hind and her calf appeared between the trees coming steadily through the heather. He raised his gun as he gasped painfully for air. He brought it to his shoulder to fire, for he was terrified of the unnatural being. Was it beast, a spirit or a human? As he squinted down the sights he saw again the young woman and child. They were regarding him calmly and confidentially without a tremor of fear. His gun dropped from his trembling hands and he called out her name.

But it was the hind gazing at him again in a beseeching fashion. With what further energy he could summon up, he felt for his gun and stumbled and staggered through the wood. Every time he looked back he was pursued by the silent deer. Every time when fear got the better of him and he prepared to shoot, the hind and the calf changed into a young woman and a child. Finally he emerged from the wood and cast himself down on the turf. Panting and retching from his exertions he turned helplessly to watch the appearance of the deer, apprehensive as to the outcome. The two graceful creatures stopped at the edge of the wood, the hind looked at him, the calf rubbed up against the mother, and then they both turned and he saw them bounding away into the somber shadows of the Blackwood.

The hunter, when he recovered his breath, went home a shaken man. Next day, afraid he was going to be responsible for the death of the woman he recognised, he left the district. It was said that he even went to America, but he left behind a puzzled and lamenting lady.

8. THE FINGALIANS

Ath Chinn
(The Ford of the Head).

The Sleeping Giant.

8. THE FINGALIANS

During one of the first Centuries of the Christian era the Fionn or Fingalians as they were called, raided Rannoch and occupied the mountainous glen now called Strath Fionan which runs over the northern shoulder of Schiehallion. They were a magnificent race of people, a warrior aristocracy whose manner of life became the stuff of legend. In summer they roamed the country living by the hunt, sleeping under the sky, eating at camp fires and listening to the songs of their minstrels and the stories of their bards. In the winter their quarters were with the ordinary folk.

They were an order of chivalry whose qualifications were more rigid than those of King Arthur's Round Table. To join the band a youth had to know 12 books of poetry. He was put into a deep hole in the ground up to his middle, having a shield and a hazel rod in his hand. Nine men then cast spears at him. If he was wounded he was not admitted to the band. Next, he was set off running and was chased closely by the others. If he was caught or wounded he was not allowed to join. Then he had to jump over a stick held at his own height, then stoop under the stick at knee height. If he was successful in all these tests he became one of the Fingalians, whose job it was to keep the country safe from robbers and wicked men and to repel any attacks from enemies.

These warriors acted under the rule of a leader or chief, the most famous of these being Finn MacCumhail, the renowned Fingal of Celtic tales, whose name has lived in poetry and legends for centuries after his death. It was said that he was the bravest of the warriors, and he was certainy the wisest for he had tasted a salmon whose flesh contained the wisdom of the world. He also gained a magic tooth and he drank the water from the well of the Moon which gave him the power of prophecy.

Fingal himself was described as having "sinewy limbs and wide his shoulders spread" and under his leadership the Fingalians carried out great exploits.

Their courage was renowned. The innocent victims of aggression were cheered by the sight of these warriors coming to their assistance with their fine physique, their hair drawn back to the nape of their necks and their swords and spears flashing in the sun. "Keen were their spears of steel. Hardy was he who dared encounter their rage", sang Ossian, their poet and bard.

Great as their deeds were they nevertheless had a weakness; this was their connection with 'other people', the fairy race called the Sidhe. According to Rannoch tradition it was this connection that brought about the ignominious death of Fingal himself, and the end of Fingalians.

Tragedies beset Fingal one after the other in later years. First, one of his sons was killed by his trusted lieutenant, the one-eyed Goll. In remorse at what he had done Goll lay on the wild rocks and willed himself to die. Then Fingal's wife, a woman of the Sidhe to whom he had been happily married for many years was abducted by his friend Diarmid. Fingal, in his anger, caused Diarmid's death. To add to these sorrows his other beloved son, Ossian, vanished into the world of the Sidhe and was not seen by him again.

In the depths of despair, Fingal sought solace in wandering. As he was journeying near Killin he heard of a lady of the Sidhe who lived on Eilean Iubhar, an island on Loch Dochart. He visited her and immediately fell in love. However, a man called Taileachd was also in love with her and when he found Fingal and her together he was wild with fury and jealousy. He had additional cause for anger because the Fingalians had oppressed his people, Clan Chuilgeadan, and so swords were drawn and they prepared to fight. Before they could come to blows the lady intervened.

"Stop", she said, "be not angry with one another", and she pointed to the opposite shore. "Put down your swords and see who can leap well. Whoever leaps the farthest shall win me", she added.

First, Taileachd leapt from the island to the shore and then Fingal leapt, a distance too far for ordinary mortals. Then Taileachd challenged Fingal to jump backwards. "Whoever does it successfully", he said "will have the lady by right"

Fingal agreed and Taileachd jumped first and landed on the shore. But when Fingal leapt he slipped and sank in the water up to his neck. Taileachd still full of anger, saw his chance of revenge. He grabbed his sword from the ground, grasped Fingal by the hair, and cut off his head. For an instant the body stayed upright, a fountain of blood throbbing into the air and splashing into the water. Then the body fell.

The fairy lady screamed but Taileachd, still holding the head, realised what danger he was in from Fingal's band of warriors, so he fled. He made his way over the hills heading for Rannoch. West of Loch Laidon he crossed the river Ba by the ford called Ath Chinn where he left the head on a knoll. He then turned eastwards thinking to throw his pursuers off the track.

Meanwhile the Fingalians found the headless body, buried their leader and set off after the murderer. They picked up the trail and followed it to the ford. They were then puzzled in what direction they should go but their leader, Caoilte found his master's head. Sorrow filled his heart as he looked on the dead face. But remembering Fingal's magic tooth of knowledge he put his finger under it and learnt that Taileachd was hiding in a cave on Ben Alder. Caoilte and the angry warriors made their way to the cave. When they got there they surrounded it and dragged Taileachd out. "Do you repent of slaying Fingal?" they asked.

"No, I do not repent", replied Taileachd. "Did YOU repent of slaying the people of my clan?" he added. The Fingalians, angry at his reply, cut off first his right hand and then his left and threw them into the lochan.

"Now are you sorry for killing Fingal?' they asked him again, but again he refused to submit. So they drove their spears through his heart.

Caoilte, the last of the warrior leaders, made his way back to Rannoch sorrowing greatly for his beloved master. "Thy words I hear no more", he mused. "The cry of the hunter is over. The voice of war is ceased". It was said that he was so sad and lonely that he left the mortal world and went to live among the Sidhe. However, in his old age, he returned to the world of men to sleep with the other Fingalians in the mountain graves of Rannoch and Breadalbane to await the blast of Fingal's horn to rouse him to life again. They say that Gobhar Bacach, the lame goat, limps about Schiehallion and the hills of Strath Fionan always in milk with a yield enough to supply the Fingalians when they return.

NOTE

A great wealth of these stories have been handed down by practised story tellers. In Ireland and all parts of Europe similar stories of elite legendary warriors have been told. In the Scottish glens, when a stranger appeared, one of the first questions asked him was, "Do you know any stories of the Fingalians?" If he did he was sure of a warm welcome and an eager audience. This particular story, although very old, was probably invented in order to explain the meaning of local place names, such as CULTULLICH, Caoilt-tullich, Hill (burial place) of Caoilte; KILLIN, Cill Finn, The Grave of the Finn; LOCHAN NAN LAMH, The Little Loch of the Hands; ATH CHINN, The Ford of the Head.

The Sleeping Giant of Bunrannoch is waiting to return. He can be seen from Kinloch Rannoch lying on the hillside in his last sleep. Muscle, blood and bone have dissolved, leaving a vast silhouette. Sheep graze on his head and his massive body, but he is literally just sleeping, and he will tear himself from the hillside when he hears the blast of his master's horn.

9. THE BIG SERGEANT

The Clach or Rocking Stone.

9.THE BIG SERGEANT

Sergeant John Dhu Cameron was a Jacobite Cateran whose activities elevated him to the character of a folk hero in Rannoch. He was a magnificent figure of a Gael, nicknamed Sergeant Mhor because of his size. He had been 'out' in 1745, and after the ruin of Bonnie Prince Charlie's fortunes, and the proscription of his followers, he was obliged to take to the hills for concealment. Other desperadoes joined him and they haunted the wilds of Rannoch and Lochaber, hunted by the soldiers, and forced to steal sheep or cattle to survive. Although he was an outlaw, the Rannoch people loved him for he robbed the rich and the Hanoverians and gave to the poor. He extorted blackmail or protection money but he promised to replace any cattle stolen by others. Time after time he was pursued by the soldiers from Rannoch Barracks; and according to Highland custom, he retaliated on the military to such an effect that his name was respected and greatly feared by the garrisons.

At this time an officer had been sent from Kingshouse to pay the garrisons of Achallader and Invercomrie (at Rannoch). When he left Achallader where the N.C.O. had given him instructions as to his route it was late in the day. "From Madagan Moineach", said the N.C.O. "follow the path up the hill to the Clach", and he described the Clach or Rocking Stone.

The officer took the hill path but he soon lost it in the darkness. He dismounted and led his horse, for riding was impossible, and he continued struggling on his way, exhausted and dispirited. No more solitary path than this exists in the kingdom and the soldier was soon aware of the wildness and loneliness of the district in which he was now completely lost, and also at the back of his mind was the additional danger of an encounter with Sergeant Mhor and his gang of outlaws. He was utterly demoralised, his plight hopeless, when all at once the outline of the strange stones of the Clach loomed out of the darkness. His relief was immediate but, alas, it was short lived for from behind the stone appeared a figure, a broad, very tall Highlander. The officer hastened to defend himself from the expected attack when the tall man greeted him in a friendly fashion.

"Where are you going, stranger"? asked the Highlander. The officer said that he was on his way to the Rannoch Barracks at Invercomrie and that he had lost his way.

"You can't get there in the dark", said the Highlander. "You will have to find somewhere to spend the night. Come with me", he added.

The officer followed him and they fell into conversation, the soldier describing how he had got lost, and how he was worried because of the danger of meeting Sergeant Mhor and his men. The Highlander agreed that he was in the country where the outlaws operated, but he assured him he would be safe with him.

Soon they arrived at the entrance to a bothy where there was a good fire, around which sat several stalwart Highlanders. His companion, the tall, powerful Highlander who seemed the most important of the men, led him in. The men received him kindly, made room for him at the fire, and shared with him their supper, and their mountain dew. Some branches, quickly cut down, and made into a canopy, gave shelter for his horse, and new cut heather, spread on the floor, with plaids and sheepskins, formed a bed on which the officer was glad to rest his weary limbs. He expressed his thanks for the kindness he had received, and at the same time mentioned again how he had been afraid of being robbed by Sergeant Mhor and his warriors. The Highlander assured him of safety and protection, and bade him dismiss all fears of Sergeant Mhor.

In the morning, the Highlander accompanied him on his way to Invercomrie Barracks. As they went along the officer continued to enlarge upon the Sergeant's reputation, and his fear of being robbed of the wages he carried for the Rannoch soldiers. He expressed the great appreciation he had for the kindness and protection he had received from his Highland friend.

When they came in sight of the Barracks, the tall Highlander stopped. "I promised you protection", he said, "and I have given it. However, safety for myself prevents my approaching nearer to the dwelling of the red soldier. You have spoken of Sergeant Mhor, but you do not know the man: I am Sergeant Mhor." The officer was taken aback for he remembered the reputation of the great man, the ambushes, the sudden attacks and the flashing dirks. He looked round apprehensively.

"Fear not", added the Highlander, "fear not Sergeant Mhor or any of his. You are in perfect safety: and your money. But tell Captain

Patten from me, that Sergeant Mhor never killed a man but in self-defence: that he never took what was not his own, except a sheep from the hill for his food. Say to him and your Commanders that had he not been hunted down as a wild beast, had a price not been set on his head, had he been able, in safety, to follow any occupation, by which he could have honourably subsisted, Sergeant Mhor would not even have done this".

The officer was very affected by his words and they parted with expressions of friendship to one another. To every man he met thereafter he told of the hospitable treatment by the outlaws when he was lost, and of the kindness of Sergeant Mhor himself. Alas, one night while taking shelter in one of his hideouts at Dunan, the Big Sergeant was betrayed to the soldiers for the reward money. He was chained like a wild beast and hanged at Perth in 1753, and all Rannoch mourned, and an officer of the English army mourned with them.

THE CLACH

The Clach or Rocking Stone is a group of granite 'Erratics' piled on top of one another, forming a remarkable feature, like the Sphinx in the desert. Through the years it has been a noted landmark and rendezvous on the 'Thieves Road' or Drove Road from Achallader (Loch Tulla) to Invercomrie in Rannoch. It can be found now but only with great difficulty because of the faintness of the path and the new plantation surrounding it. For those interested and determined, it is at a height of 1,200 feet, about half a mile south-east of Allt an Fhail, at 425 500.

LEGENDS AND HISTORICAL TALES

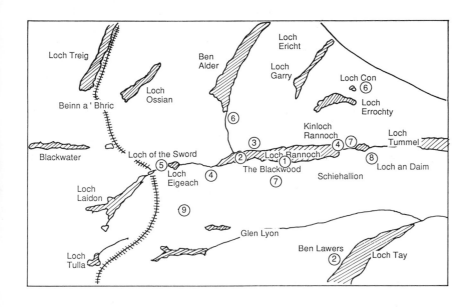

1. The Stone of the Heads.
2. MacGregor the Bold.
3. Sarah's Second Sight.
4. The Great Evangelist.
5. The Broken Heart Stone.
6. The Exploits of Duncan the Fat.
7. The Blackwood Story.
8. The Fingalians.
9. The Big Sergeant.

FOLKTALES

10. THE WATERSHED BATTLE

The Head Stone.

10. THE WATERSHED BATTLE

When the world was young and Rannoch Moor was covered with trees there lived two giants, Anier and Anear. While one was rapacious the other was destructive and they were very jealous of one another. They both wanted the waters of the Moor.

Giants are usually quarrelsome and small minded and these were no exception; they bickered and argued all day long about who should have the waters. Eventually they came to blows and their screams and curses could be heard from far and wide. They tore up the trees and snapped off the trunks to use as clubs and missiles.

For thirty days and thirty nights the battle raged. Although both were wounded and sorely bruised they fought on stubbornly until the Moor was a wilderness, not a tree was left standing. Finally, exhausted, and neither having gained anything, they agreed on a truce. They decided to divide the waters. Anier was to take the rivers to the Atlantic by the way of the Etive, and the Kinglass and the Orchy, while Anear was to take the easterly flow by Loch Laidon, the River Gaur, Loch Rannoch, the Tummel and the Tay to the North Sea.

NOTE

The Central Watershed of Scotland is situated on Rannoch Moor. It covers a large area of land at a height of a thousand feet from where the Waters of the Moor feed both the Atlantic and the North Sea. In the middle of this wild and lonely place is a huge stone called by the pupils of Rannoch School, the Head Stone, because it has the features of a man looking towards Black Corries Lodge. (The stone was frequently used as a check-point in their Navigation Exercises).

It was here that the battle took place between the giants of the moor. The traveller today might feel a sense of isolation in this uninhabited corner of the world, amongst the bog and the innumerable lochans, and, although sceptical about the giants, he can nevertheless see the remains of the Scots Pines, which covered the area about 6,000 years ago, exposed in the deeply eroded peat hags

Map Reference of the Head Stone – 327 523.

11. THE WITCH AND THE DEER HUNTER

The Witch's Seat.

11. THE WITCH AND THE DEER HUNTER

West of Loch Ossian on the Blackwater Moor stands the Mountain Beinn a' Bhric. In the olden days this area was much used by Rannoch people for their grazing. Here, when the Summer evening's light was fading the herdsmen would often see the witch, Cailleach na Beinn, collecting her hinds together ready for the milking. At the same time she sang a wild air that the mothers of Lochaber and Rannoch would use to lull their children to sleep.

"I will protect my bonnie red deer.
I'll take them to the secret corries
Where the sweet grass grows tender and green.
And I will look after my darlings
On the high mountain tops
And not let the huntsmen get near them.
But when the hunter men round my dun deer prowl,
I will not let them nigh;
Through the rended cloud I will cast one scowl,
And they'll faint on the heath and die."

When the hunters saw the Cailleach and heard this song they kept away from Beinn a' Bhric. But there was living in the area at this time (when James V1 ruled Scotland) a famous huntsman called Donn t'suil (Brown Eyes) who was renowned for his skill with the bow. He was able to stalk a feeding hind so close that by giving a peculiar whistle he could make the animal look up so that he was able to hit her between the eyes with his arrow. But he was on friendly terms with the Cailleach and he never attempted to hunt her herd.

One day he was on the Saddle of Beinn a' Bhric sitting on a large stone, called The Witch's Chair, from its shape. He had found it wise to sit here and think kindly of the witch before proceeding. He was lighting a fire with his flint when suddenly the witch appeared at his side.

"Where did you come from?" he asked.

"I was on the top of Ben Chrulaiste when you struck the first spark on your flint", she replied.

"Were you running?" he asked.

"No, only a bittie", she said.

They continued their friendly conversation and, as he frequently did, he gave her some food, and she departed.

Some time later Donn t'suil was stalking a deer near the Witch's Well. On peeping over a knoll he saw her milking a hind. He put down his bow for he never shot at her herd. She meanwhile, was having trouble. Her deer had been restless all day and the hind she was milking was nervous. She was crooning a lullaby to soothe it when it kicked the cogan out of her hand spilling the milk all over her. The witch jumped up angrily causing the deer to run off over the hillside. In her temper she shouted after it, "I wish Donn t'suil's arrow was in you". Hearing this, Donn t'suil brought his bow to his shoulder and shot at the hind, bringing it down with his arrow piercing its heart.

Cailleach na Beinn was highly pleased. She told him that he had often been kind to her and she would like to do him a favour. She asked him whether he would prefer the sense of sight or the sense of smell being taken from the deer. Donn t'suil answered, "You take the nose from them and I'll take the eye", meaning that he could deceive the eye but never the nose.

"Henceforth", she said, "you can go up wind of the deer, but one day you will shoot a very big stag. In the gralloch of this great beast will be found a ball of worsted yarn. It will be your last deer."

Donn t'suil hunted the mountains between Rannoch and Loch Treig for many years, adding greatly to his reputation. In his latter years when he could no longer take to the hills he lived in a little bothan at the head of Loch Treig where his daughter looked after him. His chief delight was to sit by the window and watch the sun sinking, and look out for the deer coming down to the water.

One evening, in the autumn of the year, Donn t'suil saw a great stag descend from the corrie. He watched it come down to the loch. He was too weak to draw his bow but he said to his daughter, "You lift it and I'll guide it." She looked at him in astonishment but he pointed at it on the wall. She took down the dusty weapon. He mentioned her to approach softly, and keeping his eyes fixed on the stag he told her to bend the bow. They both exerted their strength. He took an arrow, fixed it in the cord, and drew it back almost to his head. The arrow sped on its way and the great beast fell dead.

His daughter gralloched it and she found a ball of worsted yarn. She showed it to her father, who said, "It is the last shot. It is the Cailleach's prophecy. I am done." He died that night and in the morning the lochan near the house turned red. The people thought it had some connection with Donn t'suill's death so they called it Lochan Donn t'suil.

Another version of the story gives the hunter's name as DonaldMacDonald, or as they have it in Gaelic, Domhuill Mic Fhionnlaidh Nan Dan. When he had killed his final stag and died, his daughter wrapped his body in a deerhide and the people buried him as he requested 'near the stream which slowly moves with gentle steps'. They buried him on his beloved mountain, Beinn a' Bhric where the stream, (now called Allt Nighean Mhic Domhuill, meaning 'The burn of the Daughter of MacDonald') flows down to the Lochan which bears his name, Loch na Mhic Dhomhuill.

NOTES

The Witch's Well is near the summit of Beinn a' Bhric at 314 642, and the witch cleans it out each May.

The Witch's Chair is on the Saddle at 324 642.

The best approach to the summit is by the Stalker's Path which leaves Corrour Station in a Westerly direction but walkers should contact the stalker before proceeding, particularly in the Shooting Season.

12. THE RANNOCH GIANTS

The Frog Stone and other stones which
"littered the countryside for miles around".

12. THE RANNOCH GIANTS

The Fomorians, two giants of Rannoch Moor, were wicked and formidable and they took delight in terrorising the people of Rannoch. Many brave men had tried to attack them and braver men had pleaded with them to spare the people, but the same fate overtook them all; their mangled bodies were found on the hillsides.

The people of Rannoch were desperate; they hardly had a night's sleep in their beds, for the giants rampaged nearly every night, roaring and tearing things up. A young man of the district, known for his patience and good sense rather that for his strength, decided to do what he could to rid the area of the two ogres. He made his way into the mists of the Black Corrie, and being careful not to be seen, he observed them from a safe distance.

It was soon obvious that they were a quarrelsome pair for ever arguing about their strength, flexing their muscles and showing off to one another. Their arguments got fiercer and fiercer and they strode off to terrorise the glen and vent their anger on the people of Rannoch.

When they returned, the Young Man from Rannoch chose a tactful moment to speak to the pair. He spoke quietly and reasonably, saying "I have come in peace. It is silly to quarrel about your strength because you are both fine, strong men. Why don't you let me settle for you who is the stronger? Let's see who can throw a stone the farthest." The giants were so vain, they jumped at this chance of showing off, and they readily agreed.

The young Man from Rannoch started them off with small stones the size of a man's head. The giants laughed as they picked up these boulders as easily as a boy picks up pebbles. Soon these stones were hurtling far over the mountains. They were soon tearing up bigger stones, and one after another these were soaring away over, the moor, and the people of Rannoch heard these whistling through the air like thunderbolts and crashing to the earth, causing the whole land to shake, and they huddled in their houses terrified.

The giants, in their efforts to out-do one another, hurled hundreds of these stones. They thundered to the ground littering the countryside for miles around. The foolish giants continued this contest for two days and two nights until they were completely exhausted.

"You are about equal", said the Young Man to the two panting giants who could hardly stand. "There aren't many boulders left now . . . but here are two about the same size. Take one of these each, and whoever throws his stone the farthest is the winner".

Ugly faces sagging with exhaustion, the two ogres stood by their stones, each determined to out-do the other. The stones were larger than a house, enormous and heavy. The first giant, with a roar the like of which had not been heard previously, sent his projectile soaring up into the air, over Loch Eigheach to land with a crash as of thunder at Kenaclacher (now known as Bridge of Gaur).

It was a tremendous throw and the giant, although he had used all his strength, was proud of it. He watched his companion pick up his stone. With loud grunts and much puffing he heaved it up to his shoulders, and settling it in his hand, he let fly with all his might.

Higher and higher it went, whistling and shrieking as it tore through the air. It continued rising as it exceeded the throw of the first giant, beyond Loch Eigeach, over the Gaur and finally hitting the top of Meall Chomraidh, it bounced down to earth to land beside the burn, Allt an Fheadain, at what is now called Georgetown.

"You've won", said the Young Man to the second giant. But he collapsed exhausted after his effort and he lay groaning on the ground. The other one, full of hatred and jealousy at being beaten, struggled over and with his remaining strength – it was to be his last action in the world – crashed a boulder down on the prostrate giant, crushing out what little life he had left, but collapsing himself, he fell down on his antagonist. Both lay there together, both dead.

So pleased were the people of Rannoch at being delivered from the Fomorians that they built a fine house for the Young Man near to the stone. It is said that later generations also remembered him, and when the first Church was built at Bridge of Gaur it was built near the site of the Young Man's house.

NOTES

THE GIANT GLACIER: 20,000 years ago a giant glacier moved across Rannoch Moor tearing rocks from the sides of hills and corries, and plastering them over the Rannoch countryside. These erratic blocks and debris were so numerous in some places as to impede agriculture. If you travel down the road from Rannoch Station to Kinloch Rannoch you will see thousands of these boulders scattered over the land.

13. THE MARE

The Mare's Stone.

13. THE MARE

The horizon was dark with clouds, heavy and threatening as the shepherd and his wife made their way to Loch Treig up the old drove road (now called The Road to the Isles). They had come a long way from Rannoch and the mare was tiring. There was some shelter from the wind in Coire Odhar Mor. Here they rested but it was cold and the shepherd was worried. The storm was approaching and they had a long way to go before nightfall. He could see the dark clouds travelling nearer and their intensity had grown deeper.

They were breasting the hill in sight of Loch Ossian when the wind rose in a violent rage, shrieking and hurling abuse in a demented spasm of uncontrollable temper. The sleet was flung against them, taking their breath away with its icy chill. The shepherd and his wife were soaked to the skin and cold as death as the blizzard stabbed and struck at them relentlessly. She soon became so benumbed she could not keep her seat. He held her up as the faithful mare continued to make progress.

If only the storm would ease! But the wild elements pounded them mercilessly and ruthlessly until finally the wife collapsed. The shepherd got her from the horse and laid her down beside a rock. But there was no shelter; the wind hurled icy sheets on them as they pressed into the rock.

The husband knew that his wife would not survive the time it would take him to get to Craiguaineach at Loch Treig and back with help. So he knocked down his mare and, disembowelling her, placed his wife inside. He then made for Loch Treig to get help. When he returned with assistance he found his wife still alive. They were able to get her to safety and she recovered fully.

NOTE

> This incident gave the place its name Na Caplaich – The Mare; and the stone where the incident took place is on the path from Meall na Lice less than half a mile from the present Youth Hostel. 377 665 670

C'

14. THE HERD BOY AND THE FAIRIES

*Duinish, a lonely deserted shepherd's
house near to Loch Garry's shielings.*

14. THE HERD BOY AND THE FAIRIES

It was well-known in Kinloch Rannoch that Iain liked the fairies, and as you know, fairies were occasionally known to do good turns to their favourites.

Many years ago the country was suffering from a terrible drought. The Rannoch people were in their summer shielings by Loch Garry. Here, the hills usually green with rich grass were brown and dry as powder. Iain, the herd boy took the cattle up to the hill pastures each morning and brought them down again in the evening, but they gave little milk because the grass was so sparse. The people were in despair. Iain was downhearted. His cows were getting thinner every day because what pastures they could find were being diminished.

One evening he went to gather them in but they had strayed in the mist. It was a long time before he found them. He was amazed. They were grazing in a high corrie rich with green juicy grass. He was loath to take them back and as he was tired with the heat and the extra long walk he sat down on a little hillock to rest. He was not long there when he heard singing from all around him. He could not see anyone but the voices filled the corrie with their sweet song.

"Grow grass, grow grass rich and green,
Taller than you've ever been.
Grow grass, grow grass sweet and strong,
Stay fresh and juicy all day long.
Grow grass, grow for me and you,
Grow for everyone who's true."

These seemed to be the words. Iain listened carefully and he realised that the voices came from each blade of grass. He knew he was with the fairies and he was glad.

The chorus swelled and the grass grew greener and the cows were in the grass up to their eyes. As the little voices continued he decided to join in their song. So as they came to the last line, as loud as he could, he sang . . . . "Grow for everyone who's true." Immediately the singing ceased and there was silence in the corrie. Iain thought he had offended the fairies but the singing broke out again.

Iain was grateful as he collected the cattle and made for home.

There the milk maids were waiting for them and wondering what had kept them so long. They began to milk, but before they were finished with half of them, every vessel in the fold was overflowing with milk. The people were glad. They had plenty of milk now and they could make butter. News spread to the other shielings and the herds of the neighbours were driven up to the high corries but none of them did as well as Iain for he was one with the fairies.

NOTE

THE RANNOCH SHIELING SYSTEM: Rannoch had a very sophisticated system of hill grazing. All over the highlands the people had the custom of taking their cattle to the hill pastures for the summer. The men would go first and repair the shieling huts and then the women and children, with their cows and other animals, would spend the summer there, only returning to their settlements to spend the winter.

The farmers of Rannoch had devised a system of Low, Middle and High Shielings, moving to each on different months. So successful was this that many other areas adopted this method.

The Rannoch High Shielings were in the hills on either shore of Loch Garry and the women and children enjoyed their lives there. The women milked the cows, made butter and spun wool while the boys, if they were not herding, would be out hunting and fishing.

If you take a walk to Loch Garry (from Dalnaspidal the distance is shorter) you will see the fine patches of green where the cattle grazed, and if you look carefully you can still see the remains of the shieling huts. The Kinloch Rannoch Shieling where Iain spent his summers is situated by the banks of the Allt Coire Easan near the waterfall . . . . There are a dozen ruins still visible here at 623 686.

15. THE HUMPBACKS AND THE FAIRIES

Uamh Tom a'Mhor-fhir,
the home of Schiehallion's fairies.

15. THE HUMPBACKS AND THE FAIRIES

There were two friends who had hump-backs and they lived at opposite sides of Schiehallion. One lived on the east side of the mountain, at Braes of Foss and the other lived on the west near Tempar. Each Sunday one would visit the other and then on the following Sunday the visit would be returned.

One fine summer evening the man from Braes of Foss set off to visit his friend. Because the weather was so good he decided to make the longer journey by Glenmore rather than along Strath Fionan and so it was near to midnight as he approached Uamh Tom a Mhor-fhir. All was still and peaceful. He had just crossed the burn when he heard voices and the patter of tiny feet. He proceeded carefully and there, over the knoll, he saw fairies singing and dancing. It was a splendid sight and Druim Crotach (The Humpback) was delighted. So carried away was he by their song that he felt like taking part. Their song ran as follows-

"Disathurna's Didomhnaich."

(Saturday and Sunday.)

They sang this repeatedly.

It was in Gaelic and he was so pleased that he could sing their song that he joined in in a melodious voice -

"Disathurna's Didomhnaich."

And then he added-

"Diluain's Dimairt."

(Monday and Tuesday.)

The Fairies were delighted. They sang the song "Disathurna's Didomhnaich, Diluain's Dimairt." over and over again and they clapped their hands and they danced round him. Eventually three came forward, and approaching the man, they said,

"What do we wish for him who gives us such a nice addition to our song?"

"We wish that his hump will drop off and he will be as straight as a rush," said the first fairy.

"And we wish him the best of health," said the second one.

"And that he has plenty until his grave," said the third.

The man went on his way light of heart, and light of step for he found himself straightening up and walking as upright as a soldier. His friend did not recognise him when he reached the house. So he told the story of how he had lost his hump. He told him of the song and how he had been able to add to it.

"I'll do the same", said his friend hurrying away. He strode down the glen and when he reached Uamh Tom a'Mhor-fhir he listened. He heard the fairies singing and he saw them dancing just as his friend had described. They were singing with great glee —

> "Disathurna's Didomhnaich.
> Diluain's Dimairt."

Thereupon Druim Crotach (the other humpback) began adding his own lines in a loud tuneless voice

> "Diciadain's Dirdaoin,
> (Wednesday and Thursday)."

As soon as the fairies heard him they ceased their merrymaking and dragged him down to the ground and jumped on him and pinched him. Three angry fairies came forward and the first one said,

"What shall we do to someone who spoils our lovely song?"

"Double his hump," was the answer.

"Let him be the ugliest man on earth," said the second.

"May he grow bigger and bigger unto the grave," said the third.

The unfortunate man made his way back, disconsolate. He could hardly walk because he was getting bigger all the time. When he got home his friend could not recognise him for he had two humps, he was very ugly and he was much bigger.

Soon he was so big that he could not get into the house. He had to sleep outside and it required 17 blankets to cover him. He had to stay out summer and winter until he died. By this time, says the story teller, he was so large that 24 coffins were required to hold his huge, ugly remains.

NOTE

Uamh Tom a'Mhor-fhir is a cave or pot hole at 706 543.

16. TRAGEDY ON CREAG NAN CAISEAN

Creag nan Caisean from Foss Church.

The Summit Cairn

16. TRAGEDY ON CREAG NAN CAISEAN

It was sunny with fleeting clouds as I walked through the heather to the summit of Creag nan Caisean. The view was magnificent. As far as I could see in every direction there were snow-capped mountains. I crossed the small plateau and stood by the cairn, peaceful in the Autumn sun, and wondered at the violence and slaughter that had taken place here.

Men and dogs had fought and died on this spot and twelve cairns had been erected over their bodies. But that was long ago because now only one cairn remained. I could see the stones of the other cairns that had become scattered and grown over with time. I tried to visualise the scene and I speculated on the name of the hill: Creag nan Caisean which in Gaelic means 'The Crag of the Quarrel'. Surely a very mild name to commemorate such carnage as occurred.

The story concerns a family in Rannoch. The Laird of Murlaggan (the old name for Dunalastair) had twelve sons. They were liked by everyone and were well-known in the district for their skill in the Chase (An-t-Sealg). Their parents were very proud of them. There was also another son, called Dalta, which means 'The Adopted One'. He had been brought up in the laird's house by an old nurse. He had a humble position in the family and was not readily accepted by the others. He was said to be a sullen young fellow with gloomy eyes.

One day all the brothers set out on hunting expedition. Each brother was attended by a gillie, and each gilllie was followed by a hound, and with them went Dalta, their adopted brother. By midday they had reached the hill above Bohespic and they decided to rest before starting their hunting.

While they were enjoying their luncheon two of the dogs started quarrelling. Instead of separating them the two gillies encouraged them to fight. Then the two masters began quarrelling with the gillies and before long the others had gathered round. Soon all the hounds joined in and the fighting became fierce. The dogs attacked one another in wolfish fury, ferociously and unflinchingly. The air was filled with the snarling and yelping of the hounds and the oaths and accusations of the men.

The gillies now provoked the masters of the rival hounds and the quarrel grew as the masters, servants and dogs took sides. Knives flashed, the brothers attacked the hounds, the gillies attacked the brothers, and a gillie fell to the ground with his throat cut. Then a hound was stabbed and its life blood poured out in a scarlet fountain. This inflamed the other dogs with blood lust and they flew at the humans. A man was down and the dogs tore at his flesh. Men and dogs tangled in a mass of bloody bodies, each bent on killing the other. Men and beasts were touched by death's hand so wantonly that the dogs were splashed with blood and the humans were covered in gore. The insane carnage continued, watched in horror by Dalta.

"It's enough killing", he screamed. "Stop before you all perish". But the stench of death was in the air and the slaughter went on. Soon all were either dead or dying and the hill-top was left to the adopted brother and the carrion eaters that waited in the afternoon sky.

Dalta returned to Rannoch to tell the sad news. Suspicion fell on him for it was remembered that before they set off in the morning the old nurse had taken her foster son aside and spoken secret words to him, and she was seen to bless him. It was felt that he had more to do with the incident than he admitted. Some said that he had the Evil Eye for such people had the power of inflicting calamities on both man and beast.

'A very unlikely story', I thought, as I turned to look at the cairn for the last time. I noticed a stone on top. I looked closer. Someone had engraved a Christian Cross on it, testifying perhaps, to some such tragic event.

17. THE FLOODING OF FEADAIL

McCook's, or Ben Alder Cottage.

17. THE FLOODING OF FEADAIL

There is a folk tale told in Rannoch about a great flood. The tale tells how everyone was living peacefully in the Rannoch valley. Life was simple, and if a man worked hard there was enough for him and his family, but there was a race of people living at Feadail who were far from satisfied. Feadail, six or seven miles from Rannoch, was a fertile area on the south-east side of Ben Alder. The River Ericht flowed through rich pastures but the people were not satisfied. They were a corrupt lot and greedy. They would frequently sweep down to Rannoch robbing and rampaging and terrifying the villagers. They would drive all the captured cattle up over the hillside to Feadail, leaving sorrowing people behind them. Time after time they did this so that the Rannoch people were in sore straits.

Wise men of the district assured the unfortunate people that such wickedness would be punished; that the Feadailians would surely be destroyed. And sure enough, just like in an Old Testament story, retribution occurred.

It happened one night. The people of Rannoch felt the earth shake. There was an eruption in the valley of the Ericht and an enormous subterranean body of water surged up. Vast spouts were thrown up by the convulsions from the bowels of the earth and the whole district of Feadail was inundated and men and cattle were swallowed up in the raging waters. One might have seen a villager thrashing past the roof of what was once his cottage, striving to reach higher ground or a man in boat rowing frantically over a field he had ploughed yesterday.

"It was a warning to the wicked", said the wisemen. From early times in history this story of punishment by flood is told in many lands and it strikes fear in every heart. To the wicked, as to the Feadailians, their ordered world becomes a terrifying chaos. But it was difficult for the Rannoch people to feel sorrow for them.

Now, those who gaze on the waters of Loch Ericht might see more than the reflections of snow-capped Ben Alder. If the air is still and the light clear, observers could glimpse an entire village beneath the waters — church tower, thatched houses, fields and gardens. When the wind rises and causes a chop on the waters the listener might hear the church bell ringing-sounding a warning to the greedy and wicked — "Remember Feadail".

18. BURIED TREASURE

Ballinloan, in the wood behind which, are the remains of Drumchastle.

Tigh Mor, Bohespic (the Bishop of Dunkeld's ancient Summer Residence).

18. BURIED TREASURE

TREASURE AT DRUMCHASTLE

During the troubled times of the past, the practice of concealing money and valuables in the ground was common in Rannoch as elsewhere in the country. Feuds, cattle raids and frequent wars from age to age caused a good deal of wealth to be committed for safe keeping to the earth, and often their unfortunate owners did not survive to claim it. Some of the treasure hoards that were discovered were recorded. For instance Donny Malwyn was paid 30 shillings; he 'fond a hurd while pass owre the moor'. On another occasion £13 was paid to John Mercer, 'finder of a hoard', and a certain John Currour received a reward of £100 for unearthing 'a hurd of siller'.

Because of the actual discoveries made, legends of hidden treasure grew up in every district. The castle of Drumchastle was reputed to have been built by a man who found a hoard as a result of a dream. He dreamt of taking a long journey, at the end of which he came to a bridge. It was bathed in sunlight and he realised it was the bridge at North Inch, Perth. On it he saw a heap of gold. Or was it a sunbeam? He stepped on the bridge to find out, when he woke up.

Next day he was so sure that he could obtain wealth by going to the bridge that he made for Perth immediately. Eager with anticipation he arrived at the North Inch and started to search all parts of the bridge and the area round it. He was very disappointed when he realised there was no treasure to be found. As he was staring over the parapet at the swirling waters of the Tay and preparing to return home a stranger stopped and talked to him, and asked him what he was doing there. The man from Rannoch hesitated, and feeling rather foolish he told the stranger of his dream.

"Ah", said the man, "dreams should not be taken seriously. "Why", he added, "I have frequently dreamt that there is a vast treasure concealed in Central Perthshire but I am not such a fool as to believe it". He then described the spot where the treasure was and the astonished man listened, heart beating strongly, for he recognised the description of the hillside at home.

Without delay, he hurried back and digging at the recognised spot he unearthed a wealth of gold coins. With his new found wealth he was able to build the castle which gave its name Drumchastle to the district in Rannoch.

SERGEANT MHOR'S TREASURE

Finlay Robertson, a Rannoch farmer, was not quite so fortunate. He was certain that the famous Rannoch freebooter, Sergeant Mhor Cameron had concealed his money in a cave on Cam Creag before he was captured. So he took one or two of his cronies with him to look for it. At the cave they were soon hard at work digging eagerly when Finlay gave a shriek and collapsed on the ground. The others rushed over to him to find his body twitching violently. He pointed and appeared to be saying something but no words issued from his mouth. By his gestures they interpreted the information that they should all dig in that spot. So they all set to. Suddenly, one after the other, they were all struck as if with an electric shock. Their spades and mattocks flew out of their hand, and their bodies were racked with agonising convulsions. They were so terrified that once they had recovered control of their limbs they fled from the hill as if a legion of fiends was chasing them. Finlay was never the same again. They say that his speech was affected, and neither he nor anyone else dare venture on Cam Creag again for they were convinced that some unearthly influence was protecting the treasure.

THE BISHOP'S TREASURE

Over a hundred years later, another treasure hunter, Niall Ban spent his spare time prospecting another hill, Craig Kynachan. Niall (Neil MacDonald) Miss Robertson's ploughman at Dalreoch (He appears in the story of the Evil Eye) had heard of an old prediction of Thomas the Rhymer that a vast hoard of gold lay buried on Craig Kynachan and that the lucky man to unearth it would be Niall of the Seven Nialls. Niall was convinced that he was the man referred to. As the seventh son of a seventh son by tradition he had the gift of the Second Sight and his dabbling in this sphere convinced him that the treasure was that of a former Bishop of Dunkeld. So, he took bearings and sightings from the doorway of Tigh Mor Bohespic, the summer residence of these ancient bishops. From here he had an uninterrupted view of Craig Kynachan, and his neighbours would see him set off after his labours of the day with his pick and shovel and they would hear sounds of digging through the long hours of the night. "Some day", he told the people of Bohespic, "you will share with me riches beyond all your dreams".

He did not find his buried treasure but his frequent trips up the mountain and his energetic digging there kept him in good health for he lived to a ripe old age, ending his life on the ploughlands of Rannoch.

And so 'a vast hoard of gold' still lies buried on Craig Kynachan waiting to be discovered by Niall of the Seven Nialls.

19. CROSSING THE MOOR

Tigh na Cruaiche.

19. CROSSING THE MOOR

ESCAPE FROM GLENCOE

Early on Saturday 12th February, 1692, a Robertson family escaped from Glencoe before the massacre of the MacDonalds, having been warned by a friendly Campbell soldier to leave their home in the village. As they hastened up the hillside they heard the distant screams from Bracklet of dying people as the soldiers slaughtered the inhabitants, and the sky was lit up with fires from their burning homes. They kept to the hillside to avoid the soldiers stationed to close the pass to Rannoch. The snow was falling heavily and although it concealed their escape from the soldiers it soon developed into a raging blizzard. As they reached the open moor the storm was furious and they could not see more than a few feet in front of them. Soon they were lost. They wandered around helplessly all night and at daylight they were at the end of their tether. As they stood huddling together against each other, not knowing which way to turn they suddenly saw a figure ahead. They moved forward hopeful of asking their way but the figure moved away from them. They attempted to reach the person but he remained ahead all the time. They followed for sometime when, without warning, the figure disappeared. They peered around in a puzzled fashion but there was no further sign of him. However, they soon noticed that they were on better ground and they realised that they were heading in the right direction for they saw landmarks at the end of the moor.

Tradition has it that a 'person' called An Duine Mor, the Great Man appears on the moor whenever people are lost or in need. Certainly, the Robertson family appear to have been led to safety over the dangerous moor to the safety of their kinsfolk in Rannoch.

The Moor crossing from Glencoe to Rannoch is difficult at the best of times, but in mist or bad weather it is treacherous. Many a traveller has been lost, and even nowadays, although there are Electric Pylons striding all the way, modern travellers have lost their way. More than one have claimed that when they were quite undecided in which direction to take, a figure has appeared out of the mist ahead. Making their way towards him they have failed to catch up with him, and he has then suddenly disappeared. When they have got over their surprise they have been delighted to find themselves safely back on the path. Fanciful stuff, you say. Maybe!

A TIMELY RESCUE

In the winter of 1828 the daughter of the landlord of the Kingshouse Hotel visited her married sister at Kenachlacher (Bridge of Gaur) in Rannoch. After her visit she set off on her return journey. There was a hard frost and some flurries of snow but undeterred she set off briskly, expecting to reach home in a few hours. On the way she called in to see the shepherd at Tigh-na Cruaiche, the only dwelling on the moor, and from thence she set off alone over the desolate moor.

A short time after she left the shepherd's house, a heavy fall of snow came on, accompanied by a fierce wind from the North-West. The shepherd entertained no fears for her for, although the snow continued to fall throughout the day, and the blast to howl across heath, he did not doubt but that the hardy Highland girl had long ago reached home.

On the second day after the girl's departure, the shepherd had to attend a meeting at the Kingshouse with some other shepherds of the district. In going across the moor, now deep in snow, he went off his direct route to look after some of his sheep, and here he saw at intervals, where the snow was undisturbed, marks of footsteps. Surprised at such circumstances on a remote part of the moor where none but himself had occasion to go at such a season, suspicions for the first time entered his head, and he hurried on to Kingshouse.

Here he was greeted by the mother asking for news of her daughter. The shepherd's suspicions were confirmed and he stated that she called at his house two days ago. She had never reached home. The alarm was given and soon a party of fifty men in different groups set out across the moor in search of her. The wind was strong now so that it obliterated footmarks as soon as they were made. No one supposed for a moment that the girl would be alive, but her body might be found and brought back for a decent burial. All day the search went on but without success; no trace of the girl could be found.

At length they all gathered together ready to return, in a despondent state full of regret for the fate of the girl.

Suddenly, one of them cried out. "What's that? Was that a movement in the distance?" Hope was revived as all looked, their keen eyes detecting something moving or someone waving. Immediately all made for the spot. Here they found the girl completely buried in the snow, only her head being visible. There was no sign of anyone else. She was still alive, but unable to speak or move. They were extremely glad but also puzzled at the way they had found her.

They wrapped her up and carried her home. She slowly recovered, but one of her feet had been so completely frozen that it had to be amputated. There was much conjecture about the circumstances of her discovery. Some said it might have been her long black hair blowing in the wind that attracted their attention but others were content to believe that the legendary Great Man, An Duine Mor, had saved another traveller.

(The kindness of the Marquis of Breadalbane should here be mentioned because he settled on her £10 a year for life because of her suffering)

WHO SIGNALLED FOR HELP ?

Another incident occurred on the Moor in August 1968. Major Rennie, the landlord of the Moor of Rannoch Hotel switched off the television for the evening after the final report of the Olympic Games had been shown. He then took his dog out for his usual evening walk; this took them along Loch Laidon. He was just turning to go home when he saw a light in the West. There was something about it which held his attention. It did not look like the distant fire of a lochside fisherman for it seemed to be signalling. He watched it for some time, puzzled for he could not decide what it was. It could not be a light from Tigh-na-Cruaiche, the old deserted shepherd's house, for he knew that was hidden from view by the hillside. Deciding it must be a fisherman's fire after all he returned home.

Next morning it was on his mind when he talked to two young hotel guests over breakfast. To his surprise they said that they had seen a light last night and the previous night and they wondered what it was. They had the map out and asked him about Tigh-na-Cruaiche but he told them it could not be seen from the inn. It was the other side of Creag Dubh Mhor. However, the two people, being on a walking tour, decided to walk along Loch Laidon and visit the old croft.

They set off through the woods and by the lochside. It was sunny and the water was sparkling but by the time they reached the open moor there was a cold wind blowing. They were glad to eventually drop below Creag Dubh Mhor where they were sheltered from the wind. Ahead of them was the bothy.

They were not prepared for what awaited them. Inside a man lay dead. His provisions and possessions were around him.

When they got over the shock they went outside. "He must have been signaling to Rannoch for help from up there", the man said, pointing to Creag Dubh Mhor. "Poor devil", he added.

The couple returned and reported their news to the police and a party was organised to bring back the body. The rescue party found the body as the two had described it and they started preparing the stretcher for the journey back. "The effort he made to climb the hillside last night to signal for help must have been too much for him in his weak state", said one of the rescuers.

"No", said the doctor who had been examining the body. "This man could not have signalled. He has been dead for at least two days".

This was later confirmed. The unfortunate man had died two days previously. Had the Great Man, An Duine Mor done his best to help another traveller in distress?

THE EGG FACED MAN

There are other well-known stories told in the district of people crossing the moor who encounter a mysterious man, but their descriptions of the man's appearance differ. Instead of the friendly Great Man or An Duine Mor, the figure they encounter is so horrifying in appearance as to cause a sense of terror in the beholder. This person has been called An Duine Eagalach, or the Fearsome Man, or sometimes because of his particular appearance, the Egg-Faced Man.

One such story is as follows . . . .

One day a traveller, on his way back from Kingshouse to Rannoch was half way across the moor when the mist thickened. The way had been desolate and he had difficulty in following the path which frequently disappeared among large rocks and treacherous bog.

Just as he rounded a knoll, he stood silently listening. He had heard something. The solitude was broken by the sound of footsteps. He looked back; someone was following him. The footsteps came closer, and he peered into the mist, expecting to see a gamekeeper or a fellow traveller. He noticed that the air had become so chill that he shivered. He began to feel very uneasy.

Suddenly, out of the gloom appeared a tall grey man who strode up to him, and then passed him without a word. The traveller was frightened but when he saw the features of the man he froze with horror. He had a grotesque egg shaped head, hideous beyond description, large ears, flaming wild eyes and a coarse black mane. Unsure of his safety he followed the apparition cautiously as the figure glided into the mist. He could not recollect how long he followed but as he breasted a hill the monstrosity had disappeared and the traveller saw the welcome cluster of houses at Rannoch Station ahead of him.

He called at the Inn at Rannoch Station for a dram to steady his nerves. On enquiring whether anyone answering to the description of the big grey man had called at the Inn, the proprietor replied "Not a soul. Apart from our hotel guests, I've had a very quiet day's business"

The mist had cleared as the weary traveller continued on his way beside the River Gaur to the Barracks at the west end of Rannoch. He felt lonely because he had not met a soul to speak to but there sitting on the parapet of the old stone bridge was a tall man, probably the local gamekeeper, he thought. Going up to him he engaged him in conversation. "On my way from Kingshouse, while crossing the moor, I got a terrible fright. Suddenly, a monstrous-looking man with a huge egg-shaped head appeared out of the mist. Do you know who it could be? I was terrified at his sudden appearance. He was ugly and hideous beyond description".

The stranger on the bridge made no comment. As the moon reappeared from behind a cloud, the tall man turned round to face him, and in the moonlight, to his dismay the traveller saw a gigantic egg-shaped head covered with coarse black hair. Wild eyes were focused on him and then the ugly face broke out in a fiendish smile.

He was no other than the Egg-Faced Man of Rannoch Moor himself, An Duine Eagalach.

NOTE

Those who contemplate crossing the Moor in poor weather conditions may wonder whom they are likely to meet. Whether they meet the friendly An Duine Mor or the terrifying An Eagalach Mor depends, perhaps, on how long they spend in the bar of the Kingshouse Hotel or the Moor of Rannoch Hotel.

20. THE LOCH OF THE SWORD

The Sword Loch.

20. THE LOCH OF THE SWORD

In the days gone by the boundary between the Cameron and Rannoch lands was roughly where the West Highland Railway now makes its way from Rannoch Station to Corrour, and thence to Fort William. If you travel on the train you will get a fleeting glimpse of a peat-stained lochan with a sandy shore a mile or two from Rannoch. This is called Loch a' Chlaidheimh (in English: the Loch of the Sword). The story of how it got its name is an important one in Rannoch history, and although the account of the incident which occurred there has no doubt been 'improved' with the telling it is based on an old and persistent tradition from the 17th Century.

This tradition states that there were frequent clashes between the Cameron and Rannoch Clansmen because each claimed the valuable grazing lands of Beinn a'Bhric and the pastures around the Blackwater. (This was, of course, hundreds of years before the area was flooded to make Blackwater Reservoir). Ewen Cameron of Lochiel arranged to meet the Earl of Atholl on the disputed 'march' and come to a decision, once and for all, about the boundary between their lands. Each agreed to be accompanied by one man. Hardly had Lochiel set off when he met the well-known witch Gormsuil (The Blue-eyed One). 'Turn back,' she said. 'Where are your men? If you go to meet a wolf you need more hounds'. He decided it would be prudent to do as she said. 'Choose three score and five of your best men', she added.

Near the loch — then nameless — he told his men to hide in the heather unless he gave a signal. At 'High Noon' the two warriors strode towards one another warily, hands on sword hilts. Soon a heated argument arose about the boundary, and swords flashed in the air. At a shrill whistle fifty hidden Atholl warriors appeared behind their chief, who said triumphantly, 'These are my Atholl wedders come to graze on Lochaber grass'. Instantly Lochiel gave his own signal and sixty-five Cameron warriors sprang up eager for the fray. 'These are my Lochaber dogs and they are gey hungry for the flesh of the Atholl wedders'.

Seeing that he was outnumbered Atholl gave way to Lochiel and renounced for ever his claim to the disputed grazings, and to ratify the agreement he threw his sword into the loch. Thus the lochan got its name. And the sword remained there for years until in 1812 it was found by a herd-boy when the loch was low during a dry summer. The rusty and peat stained claymore was taken to Fort William, to a Dr. Thomas Ross. When the leading inhabitants heard what had happened they decided it must be returned to the loch from which it had been removed. It was carried with fitting solemnity by twelve men back to the Loch of the Sword where it was thrown far out, and (in the words of Seton Gordon) 'for an instant as it sped, its trusty blade turned to glowing bronze in the sunlight, then, like Excalibur, it sank for ever from sight!

(As told in the author's book *A History of Rannoch.*)

FOLK TALES

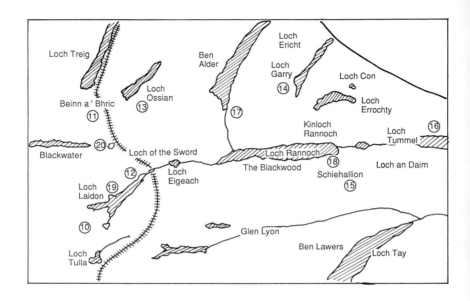

10. The Watershed Battle.
11. The Witch and the Deer Hunter.
12. The Rannoch Giants.
13. The Mare.
14. The herd Boy and the Fairies.
15. The Humpbacks and the Fairies.
16. Tragedy on Creag nan Caisean.
17. The Flooding of Feadail.
18. Buried treasure.
19. Crossing the Moor.
20. The Loch of the Sword.

WITCHES

21. THE WITCH AT CAIM

The Caim Ruin.

21. THE WITCH AT CAIM

John had never seen the witch of Beinn a'Bhric but he had heard accounts of her exploits from his father and mother. In the early days they would find their best milk-cows missing or they would find that all their cows had been milked and there was no milk left for them. They learnt that they must keep a careful watch the whole time.

When John grew older his father gave him the special task of looking after the cows and this he did very well. He never let them out of his sight. At night he brought them back for milking and put the best milk-cow safely into the byre where he could be sure that she was safe. This made the witch angry so she waited until John was alone in the house.

It was a stormy day and John's mother and father had gone to Rannoch for the weekend, leaving him in charge. In the evening John had just secured the milk-cow in the byre as usual and he was sitting with his dog before the blazing fire while the icy rain beat against the window and the wind screamed outside. He was preparing for bed when, over the sound of the storm, he heard a scratching at the door. At first he thought it was probably a heather stalk or bracken strand blown there by the wind, but the scratching came again. He was not a boy who was easily frightened for he was used to living on the lonely moor, so he opened the door. To his surprise in came a wet and bedraggled black hen. John's dog sprang snarling to his feet and he would have killed the hen had John not called him off.

The hen seemed harmless as she picked her way fussily towards the fire. She cocked her head sideways in her hennish way so that her round red eyes stared first at the boy and then at the dog. She pecked at the ground and cackled under her breath. When she reached the fire she started preening herself and then she stretched herself up, ruffling out her feathers. As he looked John thought she seemed to be growing bigger.

"She's swelling", said John more to himself than to his dog. "Yes," said the hen. "My feathers and my swellings are growing bigger with the heat" (Tha m'iteagu's m'atagun ag atadh ris na h-eibhleagun). With that, as she reached her full height, John knew he was in the presence of the witch.

Her hideous laugh was choked off as John's dog leapt at her. She fought him off but he was a strong young dog and he went for her throat.

"Tie him up quick", she screamed. John held the dog but he had no cord.

"Take this long hair", she said, plucking it from her head, "and secure him tight".

He took the hair and pretended to tie it but he put the hair round the wooden leg of the bed instead of round the dog's neck.

As soon as she saw that John was finished she launched herself at him screeching like a mad thing, her long fingernails curling round his throat, her breath hissing through her shining teeth. He was knocked over by her attack and was hard pressed to protect himself, when the young dog flew at her and sank his teeth into her throat.

"The hair", she said. "Let me have the hair". So saying she relinquished her hold on John and grabbed the hair. She pulled hard, but instead of stopping the dog it cut the leg of the bed clean off, showing what would have happened to the dog.

At last, with the most fearsome shriek she assumed the likeness of the hen again, escaped from the dog and flew up the chimney, shouting, "If it wasn't for the sharp teeth of your young dog I would be attending your wake tonight".

NOTE

The remains of the house, the byre and the enclosure surrounding the small field are on the west side of the Allt na Caim, about 2 miles south of Lubnacloch, and about 5 miles from Rannoch Station. The river has many twists and bends in it (Caim in Gaelic means 'twisting'). As you walk over these wastes you will find it hard to believe that any habitation exists anywhere. However, there is a little green oasis where the remains of the croft are, Map Reference is 372 620. It is essential to contact the local landowner or gamekeeper before wandering over the moor, particularly in the stalking season.

22. THE WINTER WITCH

The Winter Witch.

22. THE WINTER WITCH

Witches had no concern for mortals and the Cailleach Bheur, the Blue Hag, took delight in riding on the wings of the storms to deal out her icy death to the unfortunate traveller.

In the old days when Rannoch was inhabited by both spirits and mortals the hag was a familiar sight on Schiehallion. Her face was blue with cold, her hair white with frost and the plaid that wrapped her bony shoulders was grey as the winter fields. Each year after Hallowe'en she would ride over the moors and the mountains followed by her herons. She would strike the earth with her forked staff to beat down the grass and harden the ground with frost.

> She strikes here, she strikes there,
> She strikes between her feet.
> (Buailidh i thall, buailidh i bhos,
> Buailidh i eadar a da chois.)

In winter she revelled in her conquest of the forces of growth; she unleashed bitter winds and blizzards, bringing icicles and deep snow. This is when she smote the hardest; each year her scars, the Sgriob na Buidseach, on Schiehallion were cut deeper. Many a lonely wanderer was halted by her icy blast and he would feel her freezing breath and her deathly cold grasp. Chilling fingers would reach for his body, encircle his throat and clutch at his heart.

In the spring, her strength lessoned as the sap rose in the stems. She would grow weaker as the earth came to life, and at Beltane (May Day), when the grass grew too fast for her to beat down she would give up the struggle. In a final fury she would throw the staff from her, and where it lighted no grass would grow.

> She threw it beneath the hard holly tree,
> Where grass or hair has never grown.
> (Thilg i e fo'n chraoibh chrnaidh chuilinn,
> Air nach do chinn gas feur no fionnadh riamh.)

The Cailleach and her herons still continue their annual round but as civilisation has advanced, the powers of the spirit world have shrunk and become elusive shadows. However, the adventurer who lingers in the secret places of the mountains senses that the Cailleach and the Spirit life are still there, and he is aware that enchantment has not vanished from the world.

23. THE WITCH ON BEN ALDER

The Witch's Stone above Ben Alder Bay, Loch Ericht.

23. THE WITCH OF BEN ALDER

If I remember correctly it was during the night we spent in the Shroud that the story of the Witch and the Redcoats was first heard.

The light of day was fading as we clustered round the great boulder at the base of Ben Alder. The Macpherson Burn twisted and splashed its way down the mountain side and amongst this desolate wilderness of rocks and wind-flattened grass we found a level patch suitable for a bivouac.

The plan for the morrow was to have an early start so that we could climb Ben Alder and return to Rannoch before dark. Also we wished to try out an emergency bivvy bag which we had recently purchased. It was an enormous polythene affair shaped like a funnel or sleeve, designed to be used by parties who were caught out unexpectedly in wild country and had to spend the night out.

By the time we had finished our evening meal we were feeling the cold. A faint crescent moon had appeared, shedding an eerie light and the bulk of Ben Alder gave a feeling of menace, so that everyone was glad to get under cover.

We settled down for the night, twelve of us huddling together under this polythene sheet. Soon the cold struck up from the ground through our sleeping bags. Although we put our rucksacks and spare waterproofs down as insulation it was very uncomfortable. In fact it was miserable. Soon the sides of the bivvy became clammy and it was not long before the condensation was streaming down the walls and dripping from above. Sleep became impossible. Someone said it was starting to smell like the grave.

"There's not much air", said one. "I'm beginning to suffocate".

"We'll all be asphyxiated. We'll be found tomorrow, in this enormous shroud, dead", said another.

That's how our bivvy bag came to be called 'The Shroud'. However, there was no more sleep as talk moved on from grave clothes to corpses, from headless spectres to bogies, from ghosts to fairies and from fairies to witches. Soon we were listening to the story of The Witch and The Redcoats.

THE STORY

It was in 1746 and Prince Charlie had avoided capture after the defeat of the Stuart cause at the Battle of Culloden. He was taking refuge with Cluny Macpherson on Ben Alder in his 'Cage', which is called Prince Charlie's Cave on the map. The Redcoats were searching the area, having got word that their fugitive was near at hand. A patrol of four, with a corporal in charge came across a Cailleach, an old hag, gathering faggots near the burn. They accosted her and plied her with questions. She muttered and cursed in reply and was in no way inclined to be friendly. However, the soldiers persisted for they felt that her presence in such a lonely spot suggested that there were other people near.

"Where are they? Show us where Cluny is hiding?" They menaced her and treated her roughly. "There is a big reward for Prince Charlie", they said.

It was the sight of the gold coins in the corporal's hands that changed the old woman's attitude. Her fingers clutched the money greedily, and in a surly fashion she said, "Follow me then, it's a long climb", and so saying she set off up the hill, following the burn, with the soldiers hurrying to keep up.

When they reached the summit plateau the mist was thick. Sometimes the soldiers lost sight of her and it was only by the sound of her keening and muttered curses that enabled them to stay in touch.

They were heading through the mist when the Cailleach indicated that they were getting near, and that they must stay close. Just then the corporal stumbled. He tripped over a stone and fell flat. He was slightly dazed and it was a while before he scrambled to his feet. He hurried to overtake his companions and was just in time to see the witch and the three soldiers fall head-long over the cliff. He heard the cries as his men hurtled down on to the rocks thousands of feet below. Before the sounds died away he saw, through the mist, the witch rising from the depths of the corrie as a raven. The bird circled overhead and then flew off screeching in triumph.

The corporal, angry and seeking revenge, made his way back to the place where they had met the cailleach. There he saw the raven, black as night, perched on a rock. He crept up and raising his sword above his head he brought it slicing down. He killed the bird and at the same time he split the rock with the force of his blow.

THE INCIDENT

It was this story and the other talk in the Shroud that was, I think, responsible for what happened to Christopher. He set off with the rest of us early next morning. It was beautiful, cold and crisp, and the views from the plateau were superb. We were heading for the top and walking round the lip of the Rough Corrie (Garbh Choire) when Christopher collapsed. His voice was faint; he felt weak and tired and felt unable to go on. We abandoned our climb and spent the next few hours getting him down to Ben Alder Cottage and from there back to School.

The doctor made him stay in bed for a day or two and then he appeared back in class none the worse. Christopher was not a skiver. The interesting thing is that he 'collapsed' on the edge of the corrie where the witch and her victims had plunged over. What had come over him? Was it auto-suggestion? Was it a vivid imagination? Was it vertigo? Or was it lack of sleep in the Shroud? Who knows?

NOTE

At Map Reference 478 705 you will find the Witch's Stone by the side of Allt Fuaran Mhic Beathain. There is a fully grown Rowan tree growing in the split made by the Hanoverain Corporal's sword.

24. THE CROFTERS AND THE WITCH

Clach an Fhuarain and the Witch's Grave.
This and other stones with 'M' engraved on them
marked the old boundary of the Menzies Land.

24. THE CROFTERS AND THE WITCH

There were five lonely crofts on the West Rannoch Moors and they were sorely troubled by the Witch of Beinn a' Bhric. In this bleak land where the mountain breezes moaned and the belling of stags echoed loudly across the slopes, these good folk would huddle round their fires after the day's work was done. On those nights of the year when they heard the rush of the night wind outside, and when they saw black shadows racing across the moon's silver face they knew that the witch was about.

Sometimes she changed shapes and she became a cat meowing at the window, or a hen scratching at the door. Sometimes she landed on the roof as a raven, watching and waiting. When this occurred the people locked their doors tighter, fastened their windows more securely, and built up their fires so she could not enter down the chimney.

Often she would come unseen and wither the crops or steal the goodness from the grain. She might take the milk or make it sour and turn the butter rancid. Life was hard enough in those days when famine and plague often stalked the land and the drying up of a cow or the failure of a crop could spell starvation. On many occasions she spirited away their best milk-cows and the crofters would find them miles away.

The story is told of the crofter from Cruaich called Angus nan Ainean who found his best milk-cow missing. It was not the first time he had suffered from the witch's evil activities. For days he searched high and low but he found no sign of cow or witch. Eventually, miles away from home, he heard a sad lowing in the distance. As he got closer he heard the cackling voice of the witch cursing his cow for her lack of milk. He could see the thin, emaciated flanks of his favourite animal in a small enclosure, and his anger got the better of him.

Versions differ as to the rest of the story. It is generally believed that Angus killed the witch and buried her beside the little cattle enclosure at Clach an Fhuaran. Her grave can still be seen at the stone but it is obvious that she has clambered out. Instead of the usual mound that one expects to see, there is an oblong depression showing where she has thrown aside all the earth that covered her. Angus made the mistake of not burying her head downwards so that when her corpse began to dig its way out, as sometimes happens with witches, it would dig into the earth and not into the fresh air above.

Within a few years the five crofts were deserted, animals and people gone, and the walls quickly crumbling away. The larachs of stone remain, silent reminders of the solitary existence of these inhabitants and their eternal fight against the loneliness of the moor, the wildness of the weather and the wicked attentions of the Witch of Beinn a Bhric. Travellers making their way along the ancient track called the Road to the Isles will tell you that they suspect she still haunts the area when the moon is full, looking for crofters' cows.

NOTE

The five crofts were Cruaiche (371 546), Caim (373 620), Corrour (356 664), Mucarach (440 590), and Innis (439 578). The enclosure where the crofter found his cow is next to the stone, Clach an Fhuarain (419 627). This is also called the Witch's Stone or the Menzies Stone.

25. THE DRUMCHASTLE WITCH

The smoke from the witch's house went against the wind.

25. THE DRUMCHASTLE WITCH

There was a young tailor called Cumming from Drumchastle in Rannoch who was hag-ridden nearly to death! He was a successful tailor but he fell into a decline. Every day his health got worse and he blamed his weakness and his sweats at night on a witch. He said she came when he was asleep and converted him into a horse. She would put a bridle on him and ride him hard to Edinburgh and other places to spend the night carousing in well-stocked cellars. Just at cockcrow she would bring him back exhausted and take the bridle off him.

This happened every night so that he became so weak that he could not carry on with his job. He was unable even to sew on a button and he was losing trade. He was so worried that he consulted a wise person in the village, describing exactly what happened each evening.

"It's a magic bridle (srian)", said the wise man. "Pretend to be asleep tonight and when the buidseach comes in grab the srian and fling it over her head".

So this night Cumming lay down as usual. He remained awake but pretended to be sleeping. When the witch came in he snatched the bridle and put it on her. Immediately she changed into a beautiful white mare. He jumped on her back and rode faster and further than the horse went previously. After a night of carousing he made his way back but before he reached Rannoch he saw a Smithy. He reigned in his horse and said "I've just bought this mare and I am not sure of her. Please shoe her for me". This the Smith did and the young man rode home and tethered her to the gate while he went for breakfast. Before he had finished he was interrupted by a disturbance outside. There were a crowd of people who told him that a neighbour was missing.

"Ah", the young tailor said, "Come over here", and he walked over to the white horse and took off her bridle. There was the missing neighbour with horse shoes nailed to her hands and feet.

"I should have realised before now that she was a witch", said the tailor, "because I have often seen the smoke from her house going against the wind".

WITCHES

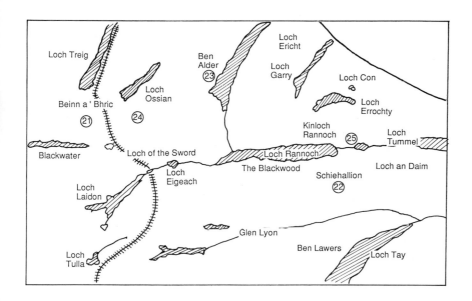

21. The Witch at Caim.
22. The Winter Witch.
23. The Witch on Ben Alder.
24. The Crofters and the Witch.
25. The Drumchastle Witch.

GHOSTS

&

THE SUPERNATURAL

26. THE SPECTRE OF INNERHADDEN

The plough was hidden on the bank of the Innerhadden Burn.

26. THE SPECTRE OF INNERHADDEN

One of the men who returned safely from Culloden was Donald Stewart, later called Domhuil Ban a Bhocain (Fair Donald of the Spectre). He settled down at Innerhadden to pick up the life on the farm again. But things did not go well for him — he was haunted. Mysterious things happened to him. The first unusual thing was as he was going to work, mud and stones were thrown at him. There was no assailant to be seen but he had to withstand a barrage of missiles. This happened frequently. On another occasion he was dodging these objects when he was pushed into the Innerhadden Burn. The last straw was when an apparition appeared, grabbed his arm and tried to lead him off. His nerves could stand it no longer and he left the district. In fact he went to America.

His stay there, alas, was short-lived because the same thing happened to him, but the apparition appeared more often and seemed to be urging him to return. There was no peace for him. Time after time he was urged to return. So return he did.

Back at Rannoch he eventually plucked up his courage and addressed the spectre; "Who are you? What do you want?"

"I was with you at Culloden" said the spectre. "Do you remember? We left Rannoch together. We fought together".

The spectre had been his neighbour and in the Battle of Culloden they had both been wounded.

"You recovered", said the spectre, "but I died. I have been trying to tell you something ever since".

He had something on his conscience and he was now able to convey his message.

"You mind the plough you used to have? Well I stole it and hid it beside the Innerhadden Burn", and he described exactly where it was. So Domhuil was able to recover the plough and resume his normal work quite happily, and the ghost left him in peace.

27. THE GHOSTLY BUSH

Drumglas.

27. THE GHOSTLY BUSH

Iain MacEoghan was returning to Drumglas (east of Kinloch Rannoch) very late one frosty night, somewhat the worse for the ale that he had drunk. A sickle moon cast a thin light on a chilly countryside. The warmth of the ale and the friendliness of Bell Craw's Ale House had left him and he was feeling decidedly cold. He started hurrying for home when he was struck between the shoulder blades by a heavy hand, pushed face down into the dirt of the ditch and his nostrils and mouth were filled with the earth that he was sure was going to be his home.

He tried to get up but he was held down by restrictive bands that seemed to be wrapping themselves round him. He was fast losing consciousness as he found it difficult to breath. Although his opponent was strong and determined, desperation gave Iain strength and he was able to get his head free from the dirt. As he struggled to get up he saw his opponent for the first time. He became paralysed with terror when he saw that he was wrestling with a whitened skeleton swathed in a ragged shroud. The last thing that he could remember before he fainted was the loud yell of triumph from the creature.

At dawn next day he was found by a neighbour completely entangled in a frosty bush. He was exhausted, scratched and bleeding but none the worse for his adventure. He lived for many years afterwards and although people were wont to laugh about his fight with a bush Iain knew that he had had an encounter with a spirit of the dead, the Rannoch Bòchdan.

NOTE

There are many examples of ghostly incidents which have occurred at Rannoch in the old days. People soon learnt which places to avoid at night and if they had to venture out they took the precaution of carrying their dirk partly drawn from its sheath, otherwise it would prove impossible during the encounter to draw the weapon. Or they drew a circle round themselves on the ground, saying "The Cross of Christ be upon us" (Crois Chriosd oirun.), and none of the spirits, though they dashed in fury against the circle, could penetrate it.

28. THE DEATH LIGHT

Balmore Cottages.

28. DEATH LIGHT

In the old days when an unusual light flashed through the sky illuminating the darkness with a startling brilliance the people of Rannoch watched in wonder for they knew that an important person, such as a chieftain was about to die. They would see the Dreag or light shine over the house of the Duin Vasal. Then it would move purposefully in the direction in which the chiefs funeral procession was to go.

Not so spectacular but more terrifying was the ordinary cottager's death light. A pinprick of light at first, it moved slowly and unerringly towards its victim. As this corpse-candle, as they called it, got closer it shed a pale, bluish, ghostly light, quite unlike anything made by human agency. It hovered over the house and then, leaving a feeling of terror in its wake, it moved along the road by which the corpse was to be carried to the graveyard.

An old man who lived at Balmore in a lonely part of Rannoch, was very sceptical about this harbinger of death. "I'll believe it when I see it", he said. He continued to pour scorn on his neighbours for their fears.

One evening he heard a disturbance and found the people urging him to come outside. "The Solus", they called. "It's the light". He went to the door and looked out. There was the pinprick of light. He watched it approaching, growing bigger every minute. When it was obvious that it was heading straight for his house, the people called out in fear but he planted himself stubbornly in the middle of the road. Appearing to be unafraid, he faced the death light which had now stopped in front of him. Then an indistinct and shadowy form became visible in the middle of it. The neighbours trembled to see the old man and the apparition staring at one another . . . . The form slowly brought his hands forward and extended them towards the old man as if to take hold of him. Still without fear the man gazed fixedly at the unearthly figure. Both stood as if for an eternity. Then with a startling suddenness the thing disintegrated and the corpse candle shot past his head like a shooting star, and disappeared.

The old man staggered and fell to the ground. He was taken into the house in a state of collapse but in a day or two he recovered completely.

He lived for many years afterwards but he never spoke against death lights again.

NOTE
Balmore is in the old district of Drumachoine at 702 594

29. FUNERAL PARTIES!

This Robertson Mansion at Dall, now part of Rannoch School, is where there was a village of Arrow-makers. (Druim nan Crann Saighde).

29. FUNERAL PARTIES!

Many Highlanders in the old days had a firm desire to be buried with their forbears and the extent to which this notion prevailed among them is shown by the exertions that were made, and by the long journeys undertaken, so that the corpse may finally rest with the dust of the dead person's ancestors.

There were many Macgregors in Rannoch and when they died, some of them who had expressed a wish to be buried with their forefathers, were taken over the hill tracks, still called the Coffin Roads, to places as far away as Balquhidder. These long journeys required relief parties to help with the carrying. Often people they encountered on route were asked to help. It was necessary to have frequent stops, sometimes for refreshment!

Occasionally, phantom funeral parties were seen at night. Often it meant that the observer was seeing his own cortege. It was said that it was not safe to walk in the middle of the road in case you were knocked down by a funeral party, or in Gaelic, Muinntir an torraidh. Sometimes you may be recruited to help with the carrying.

This once happened to a man from Dall. Donald one night, was returning home late from Kinloch when he met such a party and he was forced to become one of the coffin-bearers. He recalled later that he could see everything very clearly for the moon had just appeared from behind the clouds. When he saw that the moon was full, being a suspicious man, he dutifully doffed his bonnet as was the custom.

No sooner had he put his hat on his head than the funeral party appeared. He could not recognise any of the bearers, nor could he see the corpse clearly.

"Who is it?" he enquired, meaning "Who is dead?", but the carriers were so intent on their task that no one answered. He dutifully took the handle of the coffin in his hand and walked with them. He found it heavy work, in fact he felt he was doing more than his fair share. He complained but no one heeded him. Then it seemed that the others kept bearing the weight towards him so that he found himself being driven off the road. Finally their pace quickened and the weight of the coffin increased. He was being pushed further and further to the side so that he could no longer keep his balance.

Try as he could he was not able to resist their pressure and he was pitched headlong over a steep drop.

That was the last he could remember. When he came to next morning he found himself lying on the Loch shore at the bottom of a 10 foot cliff. He was stiff but uninjured, none the worse for his fall though he did have a sore head.

His neighbours, on hearing his story cast doubts on the whole episode, attributing his sore head to his other evening activity.

30. THE WAKE

Tigh na Linn (The old Inn).

30. THE WAKE

In the olden days there was a firm belief that the spirit or the last person buried in the churchyard had to keep watch until relieved by the next person buried. Until that happened he could not go to heaven. In much the same way in the house a watch or vigil was kept through the night over the body of the dead person before burial. Sometimes these Wakes in the Tigh Faire (the House of the Watching [of the Dead]) went on for two or three days. Friends and relations took part and often enough they were cheerful affairs where much whisky was drunk. It is not surprising that on occasions people became confused. Like old Murchadh, who was wending his way home one night when his friend met him and asked him where he had been.

"I'm no too sure, Anndra", he said, steadying himself against a tree. "I dinna ken whether it was a marriage or a funeral, but it was verra gude".

There was a celebrated occasion at Braes of Rannoch when a funeral party disgraced itself. They had carried a Macgregor clansman from Killichonan to Kenachlacher (now called Bridge of Gaur) on their way to Balquhidder, when they felt in need of rest and refreshment. The Inn of Tigh-na-Linn was a welcome sight so they placed the coffin in a side room and proceeded to renew their strength in the parlour. Sad to say they stayed too long and they all departed so well refreshed that they forgot the corpse. It is not known how long it took them to discover their loss, but what is known is the wrath of Lady Menzies when she heard about the episode. She closed down the Inn for ever, and since then the people of the Braes have had to go a long way for refreshment, for Tigh-na-Linn has been a private house since that time.

31. THE RANNOCH LIGHT OVER ANNAT

The Ruined Village of Annat.

31. THE RANNOCH LIGHT OVER ANNAT

Solas Raineach or the Rannoch Light is well-known to the inhabitants of Rannoch and it is a frequently recorded phenomenon. It is a ball of fire which skims the surface of the loch, moves up the hill of Meall Dubh, and hovers over Leargan, the deserted village of Annat. The occurrence is unusual for it does not seem to be indicating a future tragedy but a tragic happening of the past.

One writer, telling of the old days, describes a sudden raid on the village of Annat (Leargan) by clansmen from the north which took the inhabitants by surprise. The men were outnumbered and the women and children fled, seeing their homes in flames and their cattle and flocks being herded away by the invaders. A tragic happening, but such raids were common at one time and you can be certain that the attackers would not be allowed to escape unscathed. A retaliatory raid by the Rannoch men would recover their animals and revenge would be taken on the enemy's house. They would soon rebuild their village and life at Annat would continue as before.

In spite of such raids, life for the families was pleasant. The village was on a sunny well-favoured hillside where the grazing was rich. There was the seed time and the harvest. Agriculture was simple, and while the men worked the fields, the women milked the cows and made cheese and butter. But after the defeat of the Stewarts at Culloden in 1746 times changed. The Chieftain of the Clan became a landlord, and the tenant was no longer an asset to him. Gone for ever was the time when the Chief was a 'Father' to his clan; he now needed money not men; for the days of the 'private armies' were over.

And so came the tragedy of Annat and the tragedy was Evictions! Annat became deserted because its inhabitants were banished by the landlord. Some left voluntarily but others had to be turned out of their homes to make way for sheep. Sheep, and later, deer were more profitable than men.

Alexander Mackenzie writing about the Highland clearances in Rannoch said that certain landlords should be held to public scorn and execration for their treatment of their tenants who were evicted to make way for sheep. He wrote that between 50-60 families disappeared from the villages of Craiganour, Aulich and Annat.

The 24 deserted houses of Annat bear testimony to that day in 1830 when the villagers had to leave their homes. The cloverstones were gathered in, prior to the men working in the fields, the corn-drying kiln was prepared, and the stone dykes had been newly repaired to hold in their stock. The remains of these are mute reminders today of a way of life that is no more.

The Solus Raineach, when it appears, reminds the people of Rannoch of that tragic day when Annat became deserted, and as the light disappears over the ruins, all remember their ancestors who had to leave their native land to cross the Atlantic or to make new lives in Edinburgh, Perth, Glasgow, Crieff and elsewhere.

NOTE

Annat was part of the Leargan Village Settlement at 656 598

32. THE DEATH CART OF LEARAN

Learan.

32. THE DEATH-CART AT LEARAN

In the early days coffins were carried to their burial place by parties of men. Later carts came to be used. In the same way that the early people often saw phantom funeral parties, so in later times the sight of the death-cart brought terror into their lives. Living folk in their houses at night who heard the creaking of the wheels of the empty cart and the snorting of the horses knew it was the death-bringer. Whose turn was it next? Anyone foolish enough to be out at night could find themselves spirited away.

At Learan, a farm on the north slopes of Loch Rannoch an unusual thing happened. The incident occurred, according to J. G. Campbell, 100 or so years ago. One night when all was silent except for the wind sighing in the trees, the Menzies occupants heard a distant sound. It was the rattling of a conveyance (stararaich agus gliong-arsaich) and the trampling of horses coming up to the farm. Nothing could be seen in the dark, but the sounds came nearer. The wheels crunched on the gravel and the harness creaked as the vehicle was heard to turn in at the gate. It drew up at the door. There was silence. The occupants eyed one another. There was no doubt in any of their minds what it was; they were all sure it was the death-cart. Who was the victim for whom it had come? Trembling with fear they peeped out but nothing was to be seen. The yard was empty. There was no sound except for the sad sighing of the wind.

A few days later a similar incident occurred. The quietness of the night was broken with the same sounds as before. They heard the horses breathing heavily as they pulled their burden up the hill. They heard the jingling of the harness and the creaking of the vehicle, but this time they were horrified to see a real coach swing in at the gate. Their hearts were in their mouths as they watched it draw up to the door. When two figures in black emerged from it and lifted out a coffin, the family can be forgiven for fainting away.

When the Menzies came to their senses they recognised the figures in black as their relations from Appin. Their cousin had been kicked by a horse and been killed and they had brought his body back to his birthplace to be buried. For this purpose they had hired a hearse, a kind of vehicle till then unknown in Rannoch.

E

33. THE THRESHERS OF AULICH

*Aulich (The ruins of the old mill and
lade can be seen further up the hill).*

33. *THE THRESHERS OF AULICH*

The short winter afternoon was drawing to its end, and the last light came feebly through the small opening that served for a window in the mean croft-barn. From inside came the rhythmic thwack of flails (suist) on a threshing board. The flails were weilded by two young men, obviously brothers, for they were very much alike in face and physical features.

They faced each other as they worked on the same sheaf. Dughall Ban, the fair one was right-handed and Eobhann Dubh, the dark one, was left-handed. At one side there was a pile of sheaves from which one would take a sheaf and lay it on the board in between them. Immediately it was down, the right-handed suistear swung his flail and struck the grain at the extreme point of the sheaf. Then the left-hander swung his flail to strike a fraction further back until after half a dozen or so strokes they reached half way down the sheaf. The slightest mistake by one and severe injury could result to the other. Neither of them thought of that as the last few strokes were directed to the bottom of the sheaf. One of them gave a twist and a flick, and the bundle of beaten straw was cleared away to one side. Without a pause the other brother had scooped the grain to to the other side and in the same movement had placed the next sheaf in place, and the striking started again without an interruption in the rhythm. The heap of sheaves grew smaller while the straw and grain piles grew bigger. A wonderful example of skill and co-ordination.

The sound of threshing at this time of the day was familiar to the villagers of Aulich and Craiganour. The crofters of Slios Min on the north shores of Loch Rannoch would bring their cereals to them. The two brothers, well-known for their skill, would do the threshing at the end of their working day.

On this occasion, on a night in early November, the sound of the flails was heard as usual, but then the threshing stopped. There arose shouts of anger and cries of pain. The arguing and shouts turned to bellows of rage.

When the villagers heard this they looked out of their doors and saw the two brothers, one chasing the other, and blows being exchanged as they disappeared in the gloom towards the ford. The people eyed one another with dismay as the sounds of anger and cries of pain receded into the darkness. All were aware what a dangerous weapon the flail was when used wrongly.

When neither of the young men returned that night a search was made for them. When they had not appeared, the search was resumed next day but they could not be found. The people looked up and down the burn, by the shore of the loch and round the ford. In a copse of trees near the ford there were signs that there had been a disturbance. Branches were broken, the undergrowth was trampled and other marks on the ground suggested that here there had been a considerable struggle, but neither man could be found.

It seems that they never were found and the mystery was discussed by the villagers, and the travellers who came to the ford heard the story. Perhaps, inevitably, it was not long before a ghost was seen at the ford and the ghost was associated with one of the missing brothers. Had one slain the other? Had the body been hidden? Where had the murderer fled to? There was no doubt that the ford acquired a reputation. Travellers approached with caution: "You might get across, but then you might not", they were warned. "Speak of the ford as you find it", brave ones said, but most people approached it apprehensively and certainly no one ventured near it in darkness. To meet a ghostly figure weilding a flail was not something that people were going to risk.

It became known as the Ford of the Black Walker and John Gregorson Campbell records an incident that happened rather more than a century ago. It was some years after the Threshers of Aulich affair. By now flails were disappearing from the threshing sheds and the present miller of Aulich was in the process of installing a water-driven mill. (See the next story.)

34. THE BLACK WALKER OF THE FORD

The Old Ford of Aulich (Upstream of the present bridge).

34. THE BLACK WALKER OF THE FORD

One night the miller of Aulich was crossing the stepping stones from the mill towards the house satisfied with his day's work. It was nearly dark and the lights were already lit in his house when he heard footsteps lower down stream coming to the ford. He waited but not one appeared. "Who's there?" he shouted. "Do you want me?" he asked. He received no reply. "Is there anyone there?" he called again. He still got no answer. He knew there was someone there and, being a quick-tempered person and by this time angry, he strode down to the ford, saying "Whether you are man or devil, I'll make you answer. Who are you?"

At that, a threatening figure appeared out of the darkness and said, "I am the Black Walker of the Ford" (Coisiche du beul an ath). The air was charged with menace and the miller, for all that he was a brave man, could not prevent himself from shaking with fear. When the figure made to strike him the miller took to his heels. He splashed across the ford and made for a clump of trees, closely followed by his adversary. From there such terrific outcries were heard that the people of the neighbouring villages came to the doors to listen.

It was daybreak when the miller returned to his house. He had the appearance of having taken part in a furious fight; he was dishevelled and covered in dirt. His speech was far from coherent, for all he could say was "Coisiche du beul an ath". Nothing else.

On the next day his neighbours nervously made their way to the place where the shouts and yells had occurred. In the clump of trees near the ford there were signs that there had been a disturbance. The ground was trampled with what looked like knee and foot marks and the undergrowth was flattened as if by wrestling bodies. They made their way to the mill to ask the miller to tell them of his experience, and there they found him dressing the mill-stone.

"I must get it finished", he said. "If you want to know what happened", he said in answer to their query, "help me with this". The men lifted the stone in place.

"Ah, good", he said as all was finished. "The mill is ready now". No sooner had he said this than the people saw him start with fear. A man had entered the mill.

"It's Coisiche Dubh", the Miller cried, and he grabbed one of the old flails which had not been used for years. What happened next is not too clear for both men disappeared towards the ford. There were loud cries and sounds of blows. Then silence. Not long afterwards the miller returned.

The mill was soon working well and the people of Slios Min were glad to bring their cereals to him regularly. The Black Walker was never seen again but travellers still avoided the ford at night.

THE FLAIL

Although the Flail has threshed cereal crops of the world for thousands of years, modern readers will not be familiar with it. It is made up of two pieces of hard wood. The first piece is about 4 feet long and 2 inches in diameter. This is in the handle (cas) of the flail. The second piece is about 3 feet long and rather fatter than the other — about $2^{1}/2$ inches in diameter. This is the striking end (buailtean). A hole is made in the end of each piece so that they can be connected together. Strong twine or a leather thong is threaded through the holes so that the pieces are secured about two inches apart. The flail is swung so that the striking end comes down flat on the sheaf on the threshing board or the wooden floor of the barn.

35. THE WEAVER AND THE DIRK

An Gabhar (The Goat) at Loch an Daim.

35. THE WEAVER AND THE DIRK

The old road from Rannoch to Aberfeldy winds its way up the hill round the skirts of Schiehallion, past Crossmount to a little reedy sheet of water known as Loch an Daim. It was here over 100 years ago that occurred many scenes of terror and violence at night. The road leading over the hill passes close to the shores of this lochan, and at the place where it was crossed by a small stream that flows into the loch is where those who passed the way after dark were terrified by the strange sights and happenings.

After crossing the ford the traveller was followed by a goat-like creature which loomed out of the darkness in a most unearthly fashion. Those who escaped to tell the tale owed their survival to the speed at which they were able to get away from the beast. The reputation of the ford was such that no one in the district ventured near it after dark.

There was a man who had left Rannoch many years previously to be a gardener in the south and he returned to visit his relations at Kilichonan. It was fourteen days before it was ascertained that he never reached his destination. A search was instituted which went on for three or four days even as far as Glen Lyon for it was discovered that he had stopped at Coshieville (Cois-a-bhile) for refreshment.

Eventually a woman of Rannoch, known for her Second Sight, was consulted. She advised them to search the loch above Crossmount for she had a vision and had 'seen' something among the rushes. On searching the shore they found the gardener dead, his mutilated body bitten and his flesh cruelly torn by the creature of the ford.

Indignant but at the same time terrified, the people were at a loss as to what to do. A relation of the gardener, a young man from Lochaber, said he would endeavour to catch the murderous beast. So, late one evening he set off for the ford, fully armed. As he approached the area he called in at a nearby house, the house of a weaver, to ask for advice.

"Is this the ford? (Ne so an t-ath?) he asked, meaning is this the ford that people fear? "I am Cailein Suil Duhb (meaning Colin Black-eyes). The cottager, seemingly concerned for his safety, asked him what he would do if he was attacked.

"I have my gun", he said "and my trusty sword". He showed the weapons proudly. "And", he added, "I also have bana-chait cul na cruachan", meaning he had his sgian dubh behind his hip. The weaver did not understand this riddling phrase, and set him on his way into the gloom.

Colin stepped warily through the narrow pass between the cliff and the loch, his gun at the ready. Prepared as he was for action, he was nevertheless taken aback by the sudden appearance of a frightful creature. It was possible to see in the fading light that the attacker was a goat upright on its hind legs, with cats' claws, dogs' fangs and a human face. As the apparition prepared to spring, Colin pulled the trigger of his gun. It failed to fire, so he tugged at his sword but it stuck in its scabbard. By this time he was knocked to the ground by the force of the creature's spring. It was tearing at his face and reaching for his throat with its fangs when Colin pulled out his dirk (sgian dubh) from behind his hip and thrust it into the side and chest of the goat-creature (Gabhar). It screamed with pain and broke off its attack and fled into the darkness.

Colin Black-eyes took some time to recover. He was bruised and bleeding from the attacks of the beast but he picked himself up and made his way to the weaver's house. There was no reply as he knocked but he walked in and found the weaver in bed, in a weak state. Colin strode over to the bed, pulled aside the covers and exposed the weaver's body wounded in the side and the chest.

As Colin drew his dirk the weaver managed to summon enough strength to get out of bed and escape through the door. Colin followed in the darkness. He heard the sgairneach of loose rubble as his opponent scrambled up the cliff. At the top he found that he was facing the goat-man (the Gabhar) once more, for demons of this sort can change shape at will. The creature was enraged with the pain of his wounds and made a lunge of desperation at his attacker. Colin stood his ground and plunged his dirk deep into its heart. The goat-man fell down dead, and Colin, hacking off its head, threw it far into the loch.

NOTE

Bana-chait cul na cruachan in Gaelic means "the cat behind the hip"

THE LOCH ON THE SCHIEHALLION ROAD

Schiehallion was well-known for the hundreds of wild goats it once carried, the last one of which was shot by a Canadian soldier stationed at Dall during the war. Some local people call the winding road that leads over the shoulder of Schiehallion to Aberfeldy 'The Goat track'.

There are two versions as to how it got its name. Duncan Cameron of Dall said that it was the Canadians who first used the term; others say its name is derived from the days when the Goat-demon terrorised the ford.

Nowadays the loch is reedier than ever and a proper road and culvert have replaced the old ford, but you can still see the headless goat. He has been turned to stone through the years but he is there as Colin Black-eyes left him at the top of the cliff. You will find him on what the geologists call a limestone pavement. Look up next time that you pass between the cliff and the loch as you head for Kinloch Rannoch

36. THE WATER HORSE OF LOCH EIGHEACH

Loch Eigeach from Mucarach ruin.

36. THE WATER HORSE OF LOCH EIGHEACH

According to Rev. Dr. Stewart, Loch Treig was famous for holding the fiercest breed of water-horse in Scotland, who would tear people into a thousand pieces with his teeth and trample and pound them into pulp with his jet-black, iron hard, unshod hoofs. Some miles further south at the west end of Rannoch there lived a water-horse called Each Uisge. This magical creature haunted the mournful waters of Loch Eigheach (or the Horse Loch) and took the form of a handsome grey horse. He would tread daintily along the stony banks of the loch to nuzzle against unsuspecting maidens. Or children from the neighbouring shielings playing be the shore would find the horse drinking quietly beside them. The horse was, like other water spirits of the Highlands, fatally charming and the young people succumbed to his wiles. With seductive eyes and silky coat he stepped up to them They could not resist stroking his neck and mounting his back. However, once astride him there was no mistake, for their limbs stuck fast to the horse's flanks. With his terrified cargo the horse gave a fiend-like yell of triumph and galloped into the water, his hoofs splashing and pawing aside the waves. The final sight was of his grey head, mane and shoulders as he plunged headlong into the depths. Somewhere deep amongst the dark water weeds, it was said, he shook the victims from his back and devoured them, leaving only their entrails to wash up on the shore.

There were of course magic bridles by which humans could control these creatures. A man standing on the loch shore could summon the horse by shaking the special bridle gently, as he would have done to call his own horse from pasture. The horse would be nervous as it approached, and as the bridle was fitted over his head he would shy and back away, but once the reins had been gathered and the horse felt the silver bit in his mouth he would docilely submit to the rider. When he felt the man's weight and the pressure of his thighs he would quiver with anticipation. At a shout from the man, "Now!" the horse would gallop with such speed that no normal horse could equal.

One day, a drover was returning from Pitlochry to Lochaber when he was overtaken by darkness before reaching the path near Loch Eigheach which we now call The Road to the Isles. As he sat down to rest he caught sight of something glittering on the ground. Picking it up he found it was a horse's bridle.

Next morning he was astonished to find that the bit and buckles were of pure silver and the reins of soft and beautiful speckled leather. He was still more surprised to find that the bit, when touched, was unbearably hot.

He took it home with him and consulted a wise old woman about its unusual qualities. She at once recognised the article to be a water-horse's magic bridle, and accounted for the high temperature of the bit because it still retained the heat that it possessed when forged 'below'. The reins, she said, were made of the skin of a certain poisonous serpent that inhabited lochs frequented by water-horses. To keep it safe she advised him to keep it always in a crook of rowan wood.

Whether the drover managed to use it to provide himself with a herd of fine grey horses is not known, but Rev. Dr. Stewart recorded that he prospered in all his undertakings and that his dependants had prospered in turn.

37. THE EVIL EYE

Dalreoch. "They got through the door with difficulty, across the yard and into the stable."

The Old Wade Bridge at Tummel Bridge. "Take the water only from under the centre arch."

37. THE EVIL EYE

James Robertson in his Memories of Rannoch describes how when he was a nine year old herd laddie to Miss Margaret Robertson of Dalreoch he was involved in a case of Beum Suil or Evil Eye. It was in September, 1873. He remembered it well because it was the day of the Athole Gathering and Neil MacDonald (Niall Ban), Miss Robertson's ploughman, had been given the day off to attend. But he was worried about his black Clydesdale mare which had been ailing for some days, and he was reluctant to leave her. However, he set off, saying, "I'll get some medicine from Panton the Smith and bring it back with me tonight".

Later that morning when young James came in from driving the cattle he was surprised to see the old lady, Miss Robertson's mother, in the room. The two ladies were communicating with one another in signs and mutterings which he could not understand. He felt uneasy. Then crossing to the table the "Miss" picked up a silver tea pot and solemnly held it out to him.

"Take this", she said, "to Drochaid an Athain lanaidh (The Bridge of the Shallow Ford) and fill it with water. Take the water only from under the centre arch and bring it back carefully".

As the boy was leaving she clutched his arm. "Make sure you are not seen", she said. "If you find you are likely to meet anybody, strike off at once through the heather", and she added, pointedly, "Go the the river alone! The person who touches the silver or the water must be young and innocent".

The young lad went off indulging in the wildest speculations. Was she going to baptise her Mother? He had heard of such incidents. Or perhaps she was going to sprinkle the water on the "Queen" to neutralise her spells. (The Queen was a witch who lived in the nearby Dalriach bothan). He resolved, come what may, that he would have no part in the sprinkling of the Queen.

When he got back, the tea pot was taken from him and placed carefully on the table. At the same time he saw to his horror that the old lady had been tied in her arm chair be a red woollen scarf passed under her armpits and securely knotted to the chair back. It was a weird situation and James was to say the least, apprehensive. He was wondering whether he should make a dash for home when the "Miss" told him to take one side of her mother's chair and help to carry her to the back door.

It was a strenuous task for she was a very heavy woman. With bumps and thuds they staggered with their burden across the room while she moaned and muttered continually. Her legs dangled loosely in front and her head, with its white cap, waggled from side to side at every step in a a most gruesome fashion. They got through the door with difficulty, across the yard and into the stable. Once there the chair was lowered none too gently next to the sick animal and James was sent back for the silver tea pot.

When he returned the old woman broke into a veritable frenzy of noddings and mutterings, directing her eyes every now and again at the unfortunate beast. The "Miss" then instructed him to sprinkle water carefully on the mare. Nervously he sprinkled the water first on one flank and then on the other, and finally he was directed to splash the remaining water on the horse's fetlocks. He did this to an accompaniment of muttered incantations which were incomprehensible to him.

At the end of the sorcery, the old woman now quiet, they heaved her back to the kitchen fire, and Miss Robertson addressed the boy. "You have done very well and the mare will now get better. Niall Ban thinks she has the colic but I know it was Beum Suil and it was Domhall Ruadh Uillelam Bhain who did it. He admired her when he met Niall on the road with her the day she took ill. Niall may give her Panton's medicine when he returns if he chooses. It does not matter. But you will not say a word of this to him, or any other living creature on the face of the earth. If you do, you may be certain I will wring your neck".

The mare got better, and whenever Niall happened to praise Panton's medicine for her recovery, the "Miss" would fix a menacing eye on James' neck and scowl fiercely. And for many years until his neck was safely out of danger, he faithfully kept his promise and said not a word.

38. THE DEVIL DEALS A HAND

Creaguaineach Lodge at Loch Treig.

38. THE DEVIL DEALS A HAND

Loch Treig Head was a place of some importance in the past, having a drove stance, market stance, burying ground and hanging hillock. The only habitation there in the present day is Creaguaineach Lodge, a delightful situation at the base of the Crag of the same name in the summer sunshine, but a wild inhospitable place in the winter.

Shepherds from Lochaber and Rannoch used to gather to play cards in Loch Treig House, as the former building was called. One night a rap was heard on the door and a tall, dark, handsome traveller entered. He was made welcome, and invited to take part in the game.

He was very good company regaling the shepherds with his tales; stories from many parts of the world. At cards he was very expert and won every game that was played. Finally, he brought out his own pack and asked them if they would like to know their fortunes.

"These cards deal in hopes and fears and dreams", he said. "They are called Tarot Cards", and he placed them out in a particular pattern. The shepherds could see that each one was a picture of a different person. He then got each to shuffle the cards in turn and choose one. The first shepherd's card was a picture of a Jester or Fool.

"You, my dear friend, make silly mistakes. I hope you take warning".

The card that the next man turned over was of a blindfolded figure. "This picture tells its own story", he said. "I hope your eyes are eventually opened". The third man was by this time rather nervous as his card was turned over. It was the picture of a smiling picture of Death. He stared at it in horror and in his anguish the cards fluttered from his shaking fingers. As he bent down to pick them up from the floor, he noticed that the stranger had iron shod hoofs instead of feet.

"Run, boys", he yelled, "It's the De'il himself", and he sprang up from his chair and leapt through the door. His companions quickly followed him as they made for their homes. They heard their pursuer racing along making a fearful noise and striking sparks from the rocks as he followed them. The story teller does not tell us how they avoided capture but states that the Devil was last seen heading up Lairig Leacach. However, being Highlanders and familiar with stories from their fathers, they would remember, once they were able to gather their thoughts, that by making the Sign of the Cross they could frighten away the evil stranger.

NOTE

Creaguaineach Lodge is at 309 698. The devil's hoof marks are said to be visible on the nearby rocks.

I am grateful to Duncan Robertson of Camus–Druidh, Rannoch for much of the information contained in the Loch Treig and Loch Ossian stories.

39. THE WATER BULL
OF LOCH RANNOCH

The Water Bull.

39. THE WATER BULL OF LOCH RANNOCH

The first sight of a water bull emerging from the dark waters of the loch at Killichonan struck fear into the early inhabitants. But there were no red rages, no bad-tempered roaring and no tearing up the ground with angry hoofs, behaviour usually associated with animals of this kind. Instead, the Rannoch water bull, or Tarbh Uisge as it was called, was gentle and docile.

Shaking the water from its head, it looked around with benevolent eyes, and uttering thin lowing sounds, more like a cock crowing, it moved with purposeful steps towards the nearest herd of cows. Those who saw it grazing peacefully with the farmers' cows described it as small and blue-grey in colour. Another unusual characteristic was that it had no ears.

Although it shared the pastures with cows it incurred the wrath of the farmers because it was a love-sick creature, so virile and active that it was responsible for many offspring . . . . all runts. All the calves were small and they had no ears, or very small ones, called knife-eared or core-chluabach. Being undersized and with this unusual disfigurement, they were an economic disaster and threatened the farmers' livelihood.

Knowing that extraordinary methods were necessary to deal with magical beasts the farmers consulted a wise old Caileach of the district. She told them that as it was a spirit of the loch they could not shoot it. If they fired their gun at it the shot would backfire and kill the party firing.

"Use only silver", she said. "Load your gun with silver, a sixpence or a button of that metal".

It is not recorded whether they took her advice or not but there has been no sign of the bull recently.

40. THE SPLIT STONE OF DALCHOSNIE

Sgoilte Clach (The Split Stone).

Blairfettie, Glenerochty.

40. THE SPLIT STONE OF DALCHOSNIE

The December afternoon in 1745 was cold and overcast as Barbara Stewart MacDonald opened the door at Dalchosnie and peered into the gloom. She was expecting her mother and looking forward to her return, for Dalchosnie was a lonely house nowadays with her father and brothers away fighting with the Highland Army. And it was only a few weeks ago, on this very doorstep, that her young lover had taken farewell of her before setting off to join them.

Her mother, Mrs Janet MacDonald had been on a visit to her sister at Lassintulloch, and she was due back now. "She's late", thought Barbara, feeling slightly concerned as daylight was fast disappearing. However, she was relieved to see a figure in the distance. "Here she is at last", she said to herself as she took a further step outside.

As the figure came nearer, Barbara realised she had made a mistake; it was not her mother. It was a man striding towards her, a tall man. There was something familiar about him; the way his long fair hair was drawn back, and his plaid thrown carelessly over his shoulder. She experienced a feeling of great delight as she recognised her betrothed. "Iain", she cried as she ran forward to embrace him. But as she reached him and saw his face she drew back in surprise. There was no welcoming smile or friendly greeting from him. Her surprise turned to horror. She found herself looking into sightless eyes and a face grey with death. She recoiled in dread for she knew that this was Am Bodach Glas, the Grey Spectre which had haunted her family many times in the past at times of death. It was a spirit (a Co-Walker, as it was sometimes called), which assumed the physical form and features of those chosen to die.

At the very moment that Am Bodach appeared to Barbara, her betrothed, Iain Stewart was killed by one of the Duke of Cumberland's dragoons in a skirmish near Carlisle.

The following weeks were hard for the nineteen year old Barbara but she hid her sorrow and remained cheerful for the sake of her mother and the other womenfolk of the Bunrannoch villages. She was a frequent visitor to her many friends whose brothers, fathers and husbands were still fighting. But it was a worrying time as news filtered through to Rannoch. Things were not going well for the soldiers of the White Cockade. They faced greater and greater odds as their small army converged on the might of Cumberland's forces at Culloden.

It was on an April day in 1746 that Barbara was returning home after visiting the Stewarts of Tempar. It was early in the afternoon, when the sky suddenly darkened. Then without any other warning there was a loud crack and a rending sound. Barbara turned towards the sound and was astonished to see that the huge stone that stood on the boundary between Tempar and Dalchosnie was torn asunder. The people of the two villages ran from their homes and stared at the familiar stone, now split from top to bottom. They eyed one another in alarm for they knew, by this sign, that the Stewart Cause was lost and that there would be many widows in Rannoch.

The Battle of Culloden, on April 16th, began at one o'clock and was over just before two, at the same time as the Dalchosnie stone was split. The Highland Army was defeated by the overwhelming superiority of the enemy's artillery and their greater numbers. No quarter was given by Cumberland's troops; wounded and prisoners were killed, and the soldiers' behaviour on the field and in immediate pursuit was atrocious. The men from Rannoch who survived the battle arrived back, some wounded, all exhausted and all of them had to be concealed before the 'redcoats' arrived.

Barbara's father, her brother Gordon and her four uncles had all been killed. Her other brother, John was alive but he had to go into hiding immediately. He fled to the hills and he was joined by other fugitives from Innerhadden, Lassintulloch, Tempar, Crossmount and Tullochcroisk, and Barbara undertook the dangerous task of conveying necessary provisions to them. Forgetting the pain of her own family losses she exhibited great bravery and self-devotion. She arranged to supply them regularly, travelling long distances to the high shielings where they hid themselves.

She recruited many of the other women of the district to carry supplies and she organised an Intelligence system to keep her informed of local troop movements. The women had habitually to walk alone and at night, distances of many miles over rocky hills and barren moors, starting at midnight and returning before dawn, as the only period when they could hope to escape the vigilant watch kept by the King's Troops quartered at Dalchosnie and the other gentlemen's houses in the district.

There are many tales of the devotion shown by the women and the heroism of their menfolk, of the strain on the women as they carried out their household tasks and undertook exhausting journeys at night, and of the near misses as the men avoided capture by leaping raging torrents and scaling precipitous slopes. Frequently they had to move from place to place at a moment's notice as troops discovered their hiding places. Because of this it was sometimes difficult for the women to keep up their regular deliveries. When this happened the men had to risk returning to their homes.

On one occasion Stewart of Crossmount accompanied Allan Mor to Innerhadden on a daylight visit. By crawling through the heather they gained entry without being seen, but on the return journey they were spotted by the soldiers and a long chase resulted. The two men dodged bullets as they headed for the rocky outcrops of Schiehallion. They were drawing away from the soldiers and clambering up the rocks when Allan slipped. He crashed down, landing badly and twisting his ankle so badly that he could not put his weight on it.

Fortunately the rocks hid their movements from their pursuers and Crossmount was able to drag Allan behind a large boulder and to push him deep into the heather. He burrowed down beside him. Luckily the rock was hollowed out at the base and they were quite hidden from view. As the soldiers approached both men held their breath. Suddenly Allan gave signs of distress. He was going to sneeze. His face was distorted as he tried to suppress it. Crossmount in desperation drew his dirk and held it at Allan's throat. "Friend", he hissed, "I'm sorry but I'll have to take your breath away". Thankfully the threat proved successful and Allan controlled himself until the danger was passed, the soldiers moving on without finding them.

Barbara and her helpers protected and supplied their men successfully until the emergency was over and the men were allowed to return to their homes. Barbara lived until 1819 when she was 93 years of age. The graveyards of Innerhadden, Lassintulloch and Crossmount hold the bones of Barbara and the brave men and women of those tempestuous times. Although you will not find many gravestones engraved with their names now, one stone that remains today to keep alive the memory of their deeds is Sgoilte Clach, the Split Stone of Dalchosnie.

Map reference of the stone 682 575

NOTE

Blairfettie in Glenerochty was one of the houses which was commandeered by the 'redcoats in 1746. 'Lady' Blairfettie who lived there refused to move out and she lived at one end while the soldiers occupied the other. She was thus in a fine position to report their movements to Barbara Stewart MacDonald.

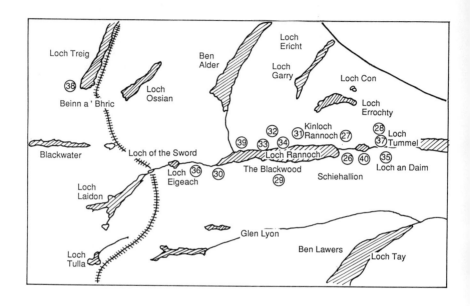

26. The Spectre of Innerhadden.
27. The Ghostly Bush.
28. Death Lights.
29. Funeral Parties.
30. The Wake.
31. The Rannoch Light over Annat.
32. The Death-Cart at Learan.
33. The Threshers of Aulich.
34. The Black Walker of the Ford.
35. The Weaver and the Dirk.
36. The Water Horse of Loch Eigheach.
37. The Evil Eye.
38. The Devil Deals a Hand.
39. The Water Bull.
40. The Split Stone of Dalchosnie.